LEVANT

A Champion Cornish Mine

JOHN CORIN

Here in the mines are untold riches, stretching down into the very bowels of the earth. Seeking and digging these riches is a man's work, a miner's work, and it takes a man to be a miner. Who else would spend the hours of daylight in the darkness of a mine — in gloom that is lit only by a candle, one thousand, two thousand feet down in a labyrinth of dark, steamy tunnels?

Raymond Harry — The Mine Under The Sea 1962

First Printed 1992
Reprinted 1997
Second Reprint 2002
New extended edition 2007

Published by The Trevithick Society
for the study of Cornish industrial archaeology and history

Copyright © The Trustees of the John Corin Estate
and the individual chapter authors

British Library Cataloguing Data

Corin, John
Levant: a Champion Cornish Mine
1 Mining - England - Pendeen (Cornwall)
I Title

ISBN 978-0-904040-71-5

Printed in Great Britain by

Printed and bound in Cornwall by R. Booth Ltd
Penryn, Cornwall Great Britain, TR10 9HH

Typeset by Peninsula Projects, Penzance, Cornwall

DEDICATION

IN MEMORIAM
J. H. T.

Ronnie Alford
Geoff Ball
Michael Barr
Clive Carter
John Corin
Mike Tarrant
Pat West

And with grateful appreciation to all of the Levant volunteers, past and present.

AUTHOR'S PREFACE

A definitive history of Levant Mine would occupy quite a large book. Its story extends effectively from the late eighteenth century to the present day in the twentieth. The publishing house of D. Bradford Barton, which made an invaluable contribution to the history of mining in Cornwall in its time, published Cyril Noall's book Levant in 1970. It remains the standard work, much of the mine's 19th century history being based on the reports of the company's periodical meetings. Unfortunately it is now out of print.

The present work has two objects. One is to supplement Noall's work by recording information and by reproducing photographs not available to him, as well as events which occurred after his book went to press. The other is to appeal to the more general reader of Cornish history and to the hundreds who visit the restored whim-engine at Levant every year.

Even the most comprehensive historian can only in the end present a view, his view, of a subject. This short book only presents a view of an extraordinary and fascinating human enterprise. The author only claims to be a writer of what are termed journalistic histories. It was once sagely remarked that "a journalist is someone who can put on paper more than you know he knows." Not bad! But seriously, I was given cause for thought by a recent writer in the Trevithick Society's Newsletter, himself a miner. He wrote, inter alia, "alas, many of those who write about mining have not had a chance to experience the real life of mining . . . There is nothing like a few feet of hand drilling to encourage appreciation." Although not a miner, I can claim some mining experience. Many years ago the late Raymond Harry was prospecting in old men's workings at Bartinney, near St. Just, and in 1944 I went along with him. One of his helpers was an old tributer, Matthy Ellis. Matthy attempted to instruct me in the art of hand drilling. Since then I have been down various Cornish mines, working and otherwise, including Levant. Having spent so many days at Levant during the last eleven years with the team restoring the whim-engine I have made the acquaintance of the genius loci, not to mention a family connection with the mine. Anyway, there is an old saying, "Every good Cornishman is brought up to knaw ten" (know tin).

Bill Newby, sometime Hon. Secretary of the Trevithick Society, suggested this book and I am much indebted to a goodly number of people who have assisted me during its preparation. For information: Doug Alford, Justin Brooke, Ken Brown, Mrs Claire Leith, Jim Lewis, Bill North, Leslie Rawlings, Sidney Richards, Milton Thomas, Frank Tregear and Edward Waters. For photographs: Russell Bayles, John Brock, Joff Bullen, Eric Edmonds, Jonathan Holmes, Mrs. Claire Leith, Bill Newby, the Penzance Library, Royal Institution of Cornwall, Reg Watkiss and Douglas Williams, while Bill North produced the sketch-map of the surface installations. Justin Brooke, Bill Newby and Milton Thomas kindly read the typescript and offered a number of corrections and improvements. My thanks are also due to the publishers David & Charles Ltd., Geevor plc, BBC and the Tor Mark Press for permission to quote from copyright materials, and to the erstwhile Mining World, whose publications ceased in 1962.

In this second edition the opportunity has been taken to make a few corrections, but the main change is the inclusion of two new chapters by Milton Thomas who led the Greasy Gang in restoring the Levant whim back into steam, and who was presented with the medal of the Trevithick Society for his work. In these new chapters Milton recollects some of his experiences of the work and also records some of the methods of operation of the engine and the history of Skip Shaft.

JOHN CORIN, Newlyn 1997

PREFACE TO SECOND EDITION

It is a considerable compliment to John Corin that this book is going into its second edition fifteen years after its first publication, with two re-prints in between. The first edition was published, as the author says in his 1997 preface, to supplement "Levant" by Cyril Noall and to appeal to the more general reader and the visitors to Levant and it has most certainly achieved these aims.

Previous re-prints have contained chapters, by other authors, concerning the whim engine itself, the restoration of 1984 to 1992, and work on Skip Shaft but much restoration of the whole mine site has taken place since these were written. For this edition the original chapters have been revised and a number of additional chapters and photographs included to explain the work that has been carried out since 1999.

Sincere thanks must be given to the authors concerned, namely Kenneth Brown, Ron Flaxman, Norman Lackford, Bill Newby and Milton Thomas, each of whom have contributed to Levant in many more ways than recording its history. By the sweat of their brows and the application of their expertise the restoration and maintenance of the site continues. Behind the scenes, since the Trevithick Society gifted the site to them, the National Trust has been the mainstay of the restoration projects and the detail of their invaluable contribution is given in this book. The National Trust provides the backbone but it is the team of volunteers and Members of the Trevithick Society who constitute the work force, affectionately called the "Greasy Gang", who have, and still do, put in thousands of voluntary hours to ensure the continued functioning of the engine and the day to day maintenance and guiding at Levant. Beyond the work at Levant is the fact that this book did not compose itself and the expertise of Peter Joseph must be acknowledged. Without his dedication to the unenviable task of composing, editing and proofing this publication would not exist. Thanks also go to Sue Maunder for her proof-reading.

Vernon Baldry, Trevithick Society Publications Secretary

St Day, 2007

At the door of the Count House: centre Major Dick White; on his left, Captain Nathan White (a brother) the Grass Cap'n, in charge of surface plant. On the Major's right, Valentine Corin, AIMEE, rather less smartly dressed.

CONTENTS

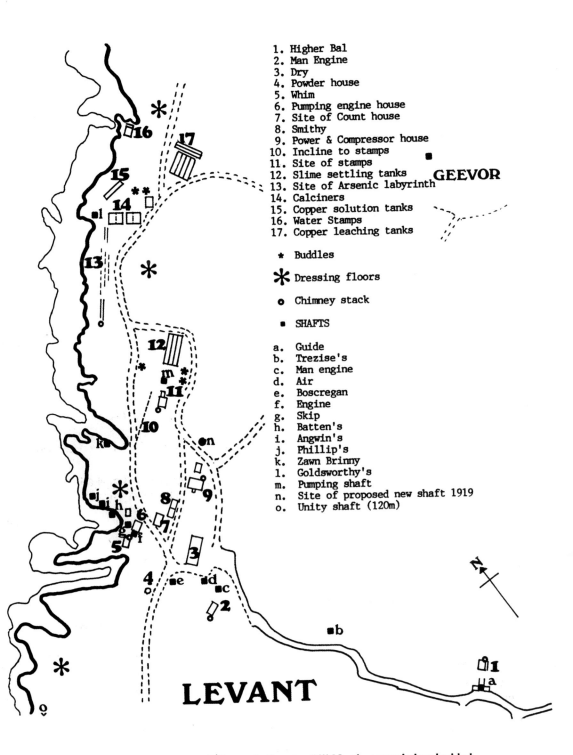

1. Higher Bal
2. Man Engine
3. Dry
4. Powder house
5. Whim
6. Pumping engine house
7. Site of Count house
8. Smithy
9. Power & Compressor house
10. Incline to stamps
11. Site of stamps
12. Slime settling tanks
13. Site of Arsenic labyrinth
14. Calciners
15. Copper solution tanks
16. Water Stamps
17. Copper leaching tanks

GEEVOR

*   Buddles

✱   Dressing floors

o   Chimney stack

▪   SHAFTS

a. Guide
b. Trezise's
c. Man engine
d. Air
e. Boscregan
f. Engine
g. Skip
h. Batten's
i. Angwin's
j. Phillip's
k. Zawn Brinny
l. Goldsworthy's
m. Pumping shaft
n. Site of proposed new shaft 1919
o. Unity shaft (120m)

LEVANT

Sketch plan of Levant buildings, shafts, etc. *Bill North, amended and added to by Bill Newby*

GLOSSARY

Readers are recommended to study this glossary of Cornish mining terms before embarking on the text.

Adit – Drainage level, generally at a relatively shallow depth. At Levant the adit is in Levant Zawn, just above the high water mark.

Adventurer – Shareholder in a cost book company.

Bal – Cornish for a mine, *c.f.* Cornish 'pal' a shovel. Used sometimes as a suffix to a mine's name but most frequently to denote a former, now closed, working. Higher Bal on Levant road is higher than the rest of the mine.

Bal Maidens – Women and girls working on the surface of a mine. 'Maiden' bears no relation to their marital state. A Cornishman might refer to any group of women as 'they maids'.

Borer – Hand held steel or steel tipped iron, used for drilling holes for blasting.

Bal nails – Wrought iron nails produced by the mine blacksmith. Visitors to Levant may see some in the middle chamber of the whim engine house.

Country rock – The rock containing the lode, *e.g.* granite, killas or greenstone.

Dip – The underlie of a lode. *i.e.* the angle that it follows downward.

Dressing floors – An (often extensive) area at surface on a mine where the various processes of concentration of ore took place. These consisted of crushing or stamping, sizing, removal of waste, concentration, drying and bagging for transport to the smelter.

Driving – Tunnelling horizontally, usually on the lode.

Dry – Miners' changing house.

Engine house – A building designed to contain steam, gas, oil or electric engines on a mine. When they contained a beam engine they were particularly strongly constructed and used granite wherever possible.

Fathom – Six feet. The distance between the left and right finger tips of an average man with arms outstretched.

Gig – An iron box on wheels, running on rails hauled by a wire rope with room for ore or half a dozen men.

Headgear (or headframe) – The tall construction set over a shaft which carried the sheave wheels over which the winding ropes ran. Later head frames usually contain ore bins or ore chutes to allow the broken rock in the skips or kibbles to be tipped into trams at surface.

Horse whim – Similar to a capstan, but in this case power was supplied by a horse walking around a circular platform and applied to an overhead winding drum; mostly used for winding from shallow shafts.

Jigging – The act of cleaning ores, especially low grade ores in a sieve worked up and down in a tub of water.

Kibble – A barrel shaped bucket, made from cast-iron plates, used to haul ore (and sometimes water) up a shaft.

Kieve – Cornish 'cava' – tub. A wooden tub about 2ft 6ins to 3ft deep. Used in the later stages of dressing tin.

Killas – Sedimentary rock, often slatey in nature, surrounding the granite in Cornwall.

Knocker line – A line worked by a lever to communicate up the shaft to the engine man.

Ladder-way – A series of ladders in a shaft.

Launder – A wooden waterway or gutter.

Level – A tunnel driven from a shaft, sometimes joining two shafts. There is usually a slight inclination towards the shaft used for pumping and winding; this allows for passive drainage towards the pumps and makes tramming ore easier.

Lode – A vein of metallic ore. (from the Anglo-Saxon 'lode', to lead.).

Lords – Owners of mineral rights; not necessarily the owners of the surface.

Maze Monday – The Monday after a pay day when work on the mine was disrupted by the absenteeism of those who had devoted too much time to drinking. Maze, dialect from Amaze, bewilder or confuse (Oxford English Dictionary).

Old men's workings – Mine workings of which there is no record or local recollection of their abandonment.

Ore pass – A steep tunnel or shoot (chute) down which ore is sent from one level to another.

Ore-shoot – Deposits of payable ore in lodes which have a limited lateral extent but dip downwards.

Pare – A group of two or more miners, headed by a "taker", who makes bargains with the management and divides the pay. As the lodes in the Pendeen - St. Just area are narrow, Levant pares would not number as many as twelve.

Pitwork – The term used to describe the pump rods, rising main, shaft guides and any other structures within a shaft.

Rand – The gold mining area in South Africa around Johannesburg.

Smeach – Smoke produced by explosion or combustion.

Sollar – A wooden platform or floor of boards.

Stamps – A mechanical device for crushing ore-bearing rock to a fine sand. Heavy vertically-mounted beams or iron rods carrying cast or forged iron heads were sequentially lifted and dropped onto the ore beneath them by a series of cams mounted on a rotating drum.

Stannary – Administrative district in which tin production took place.

Stoping – Cutting a lode away in steps, either upwards (overhand stoping), or downwards (underhand stoping).

Strike – The direction (or bearing) which a lode follows across country.

Stuggy – Short and thick set person.

Taker – The head or foreman of a gang of miners.

Tow rag – Stock-fish, usually cod, dried and preserved by the sun.

Tributers – Self-employed miners, who receive a fraction of the value of the ore they raise.

Tutworkers – Miners paid a fixed price per fathom driven.

Whim or winding engine – Steam engine used for haulage.

Winze – A shaft connecting two levels, but not reaching the surface, which is excavated downwards – the opposite of a raise, which is excavated upwards.

Zawn – A chasm, large or small, in the cliff, *e.g.* Levant Zawn, caused by erosion along a lode or other line of weakness.

THE MINE ON THE ZAWNS

The mine itself must ever remain an emblem of all that man may achieve by way of determination and pluck in wresting the closely-guarded treasures of Nature from beneath both earth and sea.

A. K. Hamilton Jenkin on Levant in the Mining World 1930

CHAPTER ONE

One imagines, a century ago, a small coastal sailing vessel creeping close inshore along the north coast of West Penwith in fine weather. The wind is fair for the Land's End, but she is close inshore to cheat the tide. For another hour it is against her, but close in, friction with the shore slows it. On board is a young sailor, new to the sea and this coast, on his first voyage. Many things will be new and strange to him, a great roaring noise, and not least the sight of curious buildings and tall chimneys almost on the cliff edge. From two of them great iron beams protrude and move up and down in a slow deliberate motion. The cliffs are high and menacing. Their proximity is alarming to the young sailor but he is favoured with a brief explanation of the course, together with some enlightenment on the cliff top, for the famous Levant Mine is known to older members of the crew. Perhaps what none of them quite appreciate is that two or three hundred fathoms below them, miners are at work in the submarine part of the mine, which extends a mile out under the sea.

Even today, when there is but little left of Levant's extensive buildings, the sight of the remains must be somewhat astonishing to the visitor who finds but little space to step between the remaining complete engine house and the yawning Boscregan Zawn. The site is some seven miles from the port and railhead at Penzance and in both summer and winter the visitor may be in a thick fog on reaching half way to Levant. Remoteness was indeed one of the many difficulties the mine faced in its history, nevertheless it was one of Cornwall's Champion Mines, as they were known. Some explanation of this term is needed. A significant defect of the Cornish mining economy stemmed from the individualist nature of the Cornish Celt. Edward Gibbon (1737-1794) commented that the Celts have 'the love of freedom without the spirit of union', and this is very true of the Cornishman. Every little group of adventurers, as they were called, in the industry if they found a lode of tin or copper tended to go their own way. They invested in pumping, winding and stamping machinery on the basis of an incurable optimism, not always by any means justified. Often such mines were abandoned after a few years and perhaps re-opened, sometimes more than once by other optimists. Modern methods of prospecting and quantifying prospects were absent but optimism was not, together with an incurable desire to gamble on mining prospects. As a consequence there were hundreds of mines in the county which came to very little in the end. On the other hand there were plenty of mines lucky enough to be located in an area where several lodes were found and these were sufficiently profitable and well-managed to last many years. In the case of Levant it endured for one hundred and ten years, even though good management was often lacking. Such mines, Dolcoath, Fowey Consols, South Crofty, Tresavean and South Caradon, were known as Champion Mines in their time, and Levant qualified as one too.

Levant's location may be said to have been dictated 300 million years ago. In Carboniferous or early Permian times molten granite domes intruded into the sedimentary rocks of the south-west peninsula.

A series of granite domes was formed from Dartmoor westward to the Isles of Scilly and beyond. The Land's End granite mass is one example. It forms the upland core of West Penwith. The main mineralisation caused by the granite upsurge occurs on the edges of the mass in the St Just and St Ives mining districts. The only notable exception is Ding Dong Mine in the bottom of the tin zone, whose restored engine house in the middle of the granite upland is a conspicuous feature. Levant stands exactly on the junction of the granite and the killas, the name by which the slatey sedimentary rocks are known in Cornwall. The junction is approximately parallel with the cliffs but dips seaward so that most of the submarine section is in the killas and igneous greenstone.

The principal metals mined in the St Just area are tin and copper, with small occurrences of antimony, arsenic, bismuth, cobalt, gold, iron, lead, molybdenum, quartz, silver, tourmaline, tungsten, uranium and zinc. In 1912 Levant returned 4 ozs of gold and 5,278 ozs of silver associated with copper ore.

In the St Just mining district there were probably more lodes in the cliffs than in any part of the world. The Levant Zawn, Zawn Brinney and Boscregan Zawn were probably made where deposits of soft lode material were eroded by the sea. And there is now a body of opinion that such lodes may have been worked, especially for copper, in prehistoric times, though the earliest record of copper from the area is from an un-named mine in St Just in 1585. From the Levant area a specimen of copper ore is recorded from Boscregan from about 1670. That mine sold three tons of copper ore in 1783, while in 1790-93 Levant sold 38 tons; its last sale, of 10 tons realising £13 3s per ton, was made in March 1793. There is no record of output for Zawn Brinney (the Cornish for Limpets' Cleft), though Levant sold five tons of copper ore for £17 2s per ton in 1801.

The Levant lodes are numerous and account for the richness and longevity of the mine. They strike approximately NW to SE, and although narrow are rich in tin content, particularly under the sea. The principal ones are the Prince of Wales, North, Old Bal or Trebilcock's, South and Treglown's. Those with personal names are probably named after the men who discovered them. Under the sea the North and South lodes unite to form the mine's principal ore-shoot, extending some 3,000 feet in length. In the 278 fathom level was a carbona, a large irregularly-shaped mass of mineral, which was completely excavated in the early years of this century, leaving a great cavern. Each man on the mine was given a gold sovereign out of the proceeds. In general, the lode system presents a considerable complexity.

THE COST BOOK AND THE ADVENTURERS

If there could also be an alteration brought about in the law by which the shareholder would be liable only for his proportion of any liabilities that might be incurred the cost book company would be the most perfect form of association for any industrial or commercial purpose, which has ever yet been applied.

Charles Thomas, Company Secretary, Auctioneer and Share Dealer.
Mining Fields of the West 1871

CHAPTER TWO

Levant mine appears on Martyn's map of 1748. So it would seem that the old Zawn Brinney, Boscregan and Wheal Unity mines had already been amalgamated for working. Certainly Boscregan and Unity are shafts in Levant. In 1909 a writer in the Mining World, quoting "one of the official books of reference" in the library of the Royal Geological Society of Cornwall in Penzance, stated that at its last working Wheal Unity yielded tin and "horn red and native silver, bismuth, ores of uranium and arsenicate [sic] of cobalt.". The mine was only 70 fathoms deep and the lode in the shaft was 3½ feet wide, quite rich enough to pay all costs.

Records of Levant proper begin about 1819 or 1820. A group of twenty adventurers formed a company divided into 80 shares on which £5 per share was called up. Two of the principals were Lewis Charles Daubuz of Penzance (and later of Killiow in Kea), and John Batten, also of Penzance and a banker, both tin smelters. Batten was known as "The King of St Just" as he had several interests in mines there. They struck a big deposit of copper ore when they cut the lode at the 20 fathom level, a lode that had eluded the previous company. In one period of two months £4,630 was paid in dividends which on an outlay of £400 represented a return of 1,157%! The origin of the name Levant is lost; in an earlier century Levant, referring to the eastern Mediterranean, was synonymous with riches, and by 1567, in the reign of the first Elizabeth, there was a Levant company trading there. Adventurers were nothing if not optimists, and in the early years of the Levant mine their optimism in its production of riches was justified. By the year 1870 the mine had sold £1 million worth of ores.

In that year, however, the mine was very much run down and its equipment was antiquated. This may be attributed to the cost-book system. This system was common in Cornwall until limited liability arrived in 1857, and Levant was the last to depart from it, in 1920, which was of a piece with the conservative outlook which held sway in the management in its latter days. A broad definition of a cost-book company, which developed from early informal origins, is a partnership in transferable shares, without limit to the number of partners, each of whom had unlimited liability for the company's debts. Shareholders or adventurers paid calls or demands for money on their shares as required to settle the mine's debts, or shared the profits, in direct proportion to their holding in the mine – the greater the holding the greater the profits or losses. As this was before the days of banks, the adventurers met monthly and divided costs or profits down to (almost) the last farthing. With the lack of prospecting techniques, apart from digging holes in search of lodes, this enabled companies to feel their way ahead cautiously and to spend only small sums as they went along.

Originally the periodical meetings of adventurers, at which detailed accounts were presented, took place once a month, but as time progressed it was found inconvenient, and the periods were increased to two and three and finally four months. An Act of 1887 provided that meetings were to be held at least every sixteen weeks. By this time most purchases of materials were made on credit, and bills were not always paid when due. The accounting was simple, and lacked a capital account, so all purchases were made out of income or out of calls made on the shares. In fact, there was only one kind of "money", cash. But although this might horrify present-day accountants, cost-book accounts gave detail which would put modern mining companies to shame.

In the foreground the tramway from the ore sorting area on the right. The tramway led to the stamps. Apart from the tall pumping engine house other buildings on the left are difficult to identify, except the explosives house in the distance.

Morrab House Library, Penzance

In the last century the cost-book system, which over the years had been constantly changing and adapting to meet the changes in mining, and which was admirably suited to the needs of small mines, proved unsuitable for large mines owing to its unlimited liability and to the risk of having adventurers who might default if a call was made on their shares. In small mines, where everyone knew everyone else these problems did not arise, and in the smallest the manager often acted as purser or book-keeper as well. But as a mine grew in size and importance the duties of manager and purser were separated, and it became common (though not universal) to appoint a committee of management from among the adventurers, who appointed two of their number to audit each set of accounts. The purser, whose duties would now correspond to those of a company secretary, through his contact with the adventurers and with the committee of management, came to exert great influence, although his experience of mining might be slight or non-existent.

When Levant was started its first manager, Captain Henry Boyns, acted as purser as well. On his death in 1830 William Angwin took over the office, and, after several changes by the old company Major Richard (Dick) White (of whom more later) became purser and effectively the chief executive of the mine. It was said of him that he never went under ground however this is untrue. In June 1840, as a boy, he was buried under 5 fathoms of rubbish that had fallen down a shaft and it required the exertions of several men over several hours to extract him. Of course it is entirely possible that he never worked underground again after this! Meanwhile, in the early 1830s the original 80 shares were subdivided

4

into 160ths. In 1830 2-80ths sold for £300, and in 1836, after the mine had struck rich a 1-80th share sold for £1,050.

Quite early on there appeared a division between "in-adventurers" and "out-adventurers". The former had an interest in supplying the mine with materials, coal, timber, etc., whose cost was credited against calls on their shares. Once profitable the mine paid cash for its purchases, with a discount for prompt payment, and the in-adventurers did well out of it.

In the early 1880s there was something of a scandal over the quality of coal being supplied to Levant, as the in-adventurer involved had picked out all the large lumps for himself before weighing off coal for the mine, and he was obliged to resign. The out-adventurers, by contrast, had to content themselves with the dividends (or calls) on their shares, and played no part in the management of the mine. Some of these were called "knife and fork adventurers". For the good liver of limited means it was worth buying just a single share in a prosperous company to enable him to wield a knife and fork at the account-house dinners which followed the periodical meetings. A stockbroker friend says this was sound investment practice, that of spreading the risk over a number of mines, and that this is still a basic tenet of investment theory. Knife and fork shareholders are not unknown to this day.

Captain Francis (Frank) Oats. *Mrs Claire Leith Collection*

SHAFTS, ENGINES and PLANT

(For the industrial archaeologist)

To stand amid the chaos of such a complex as the Levant Mine in all its stark abandonment is to realise with a shattering effect the sheer immensity of the task that lies before him. The challenge, as he sits down among the wreckage, is two-fold: to see again the complex of buildings growing as they did before the eyes of the engineers and the craftsmen; and then to visualise the natural landscape as it was before they occupied it and adapted it to their own needs.

> A. C. Todd and Peter Laws. The Industrial Archaeology of Cornwall. 1972.

CHAPTER THREE

Improvident though some cost-book companies might have been, an exception was Levant, which ultimately covered a large area with what we could now call a complex of buildings and plant. And complex is the interpretation of the remains today. The site extends in a rough rectangle about half a mile parallel with the cliffs and about a quarter of a mile inland.

The principal shafts worked by machinery were the pumping-engine shaft (known as Engine Shaft), the Skip Shaft, and the Man-Engine Shaft, plus Guide Shaft to the south-east of the main workings at the part of the mine, first known as Spearne Consols and, after its incorporation into Levant in 1877, as Higher Bal. Other shafts were Phillip's, Unity, Boscregan, Angwin's, Tresize's, Goldsworthy's, Guide and Batten's. The first-named was so close to the base of the cliff that at one stage the sea broke in and the shaft was filled. Horse whims served the first two named and the plats survive.

Skip Shaft, whose earlier name has been lost, was used for hauling and was served by the winding or whim-engine. It was also very close to the cliff edge, and, curiously, only a matter of feet away from the pumping shaft. The two are adjacent to the whim-engine house, whose whim is now undergoing restoration, and the ruins of the pumping-engine house. Levant, unlike many Cornish mines further inland, had no great water problem. Granite may be thought to be an impervious rock, but this is only true of the fine quality granite. In the whim-engine house it may be observed in the top chamber that the weather side wall is damp in winter, because the building is of inferior granite. When the engine was in steam, of course, the damp was kept at bay. However, the main part of the mine's underground workings are under the sea and in the impervious greenstone and killas. There was no significant ingress of sea-water until after the mine closed in 1930. Moreover, there was no great range of abandoned water-filled workings nearby from which water might come. Consequently Levant was able to make do with a Cornish pumping-engine having the comparatively small cylinder diameter of 45 inches, whereas in mines further east they had 80-inch, 90-inch or even 100-inch cylinders. Again, the whim-engine is quite small, a 27-inch as it has now proved to be, and not a 24-inch as often stated. But it only had to lift one-ton skips of ore and not a great weight of counter-balanced pump rods. Before the whim-engine became the sole means of raising ore from the mine there were several horse-whims. This was fairly usual in mines which were rich at shallow depths. The shallow shafts sunk in the mine's early years, however, seem to bear little relationship to its long-term needs, and are characteristic of the lack of foresight on the part of the management for much of the mine's life. Thus Batten's and Phillips' Shafts were sunk close to high water mark in Levant Zawn, and possibly another was sunk in Zawn Brinney to the north-east. There is another shaft visible near sea level in the vicinity of Carn Du (Black Rock) to the south-west. Sinking a shaft at the foot of the cliffs obviously involved less labour and expense, but was a doubtful expedient, as it complicated the use of winding or pumping engines. The supposition is that originally these shafts were served by horse-whims, as also the shafts sited a little way inland, Daubuz's and Trezise's, the first-named being adjacent to the spot where visitors park their cars.

Subsequently Daubuz's Shaft was used for the man-engine. This extraordinary device for raising and lowering men in a mine was invented in the Hartz Mountains in Germany. Pumping in a mine there had been rendered

Above: The man engine rod at one of the twelve-foot interval sollars. One of the steps can just be discerned and a hand-hold on the right. In the back-ground a handle of the knocker line communicating with the engine-men.

Private collection.

Miners on the steps of the dry. Top right, Richard Grenfell, 'Dick Marker', who tallied men onto the man engine.

Jack Corin Collection.

unnecessary by the driving of an adit into it from the valley. The engineer therefore suggested that the pump rods, provided with steps and platforms alongside, could be adapted for raising and lowering men. The first Cornish man-engine was introduced into Tresavean Mine in Gwennap in 1842; Levant, in 1855-56, being the fourth or fifth example. In 1898 its man-engine was extended down to the 266 fathom level.

The man-engine reduced the maximum ascending or descending time to half an hour, so that less time was lost getting to and from work, but it still compared unfavourably with the later cage or skip man-haulage. The first engine to drive it had a 20-inch cylinder and a 3-foot 8-inch stroke, worked at four strokes a minute. It had a horizontal axle so that it could be used as a whim-engine through a clutch device, when not employed working the man-engine, which was only needed for parts of the day. It is assumed that it hauled from Boscregan and Trezise's Shafts. The mechanics of such a contraption must have been a matter of wonder, and one must pause to regret that the ingenious mind which conceived it could not have been directed into channels more suited to evolution of more conventional devices. In 1893 the beam engine working it was replaced by a horizontal tandem compound condensing engine, with a 5-foot stroke and cylinders of 18-inch and 30-inch diameter. Its benefit to the miners and to the mine's production may be expressed in the following terms. In mines with only ladder-ways the miner might climb upwards of 1,200 feet a day, and that labour alone would equal the maximum permitted in a prison treadmill and did not take into account the working of a shift. So while Dr Johnson, the great lexicographer (1709-84) might say that for a sailor "being in a ship is like being in jail, with the chance of being drowned", he could have made a similar comparison between a Cornish miner's life and that of a prisoner on a treadmill. Certainly climbing ladders promoted pulmonary diseases before the mining industry invented, in effect, silicosis. That was caused by inhaling the silica dust raised by the early waterless pneumatic drills.

In addition there are indications that the engine driving the copper crusher, about thirty yards north-east of the pumping-engine, would also have been able to haul from all or any of the shafts in Levant Zawn.

At the Higher Bal section of the mine, some way up Levant Road, the 35-inch engine both pumped and wound. The latter function could be clutched out. The abandoned engine house is a fine example and the wall against the road, with its flight of granite steps and ore chutes, is impressive.

In the shafts sunk from the surface in Levant the engineers had a peculiarity to cope with, typical of older Cornish mines. The shafts were not vertical, as on modern mines, but followed the dip of the lode, which was neither vertical nor free of change. This was obviously an economical procedure when mining proceeded by the most laborious manner of hand-drilling. It was said that the Skip Shaft paid for itself when sunk. Nevertheless it suffered several changes of direction, and is a good example of what was known as a corkscrew shaft. Had the expense of swiping or straightening and enlarging it ever been undertaken the history of the mine's last few decades might have been vastly different. The shafts for the pumping-engine and the man-engine presented similar difficulties.

The shafts sunk from the surface were not the only ones in the mine. The submarine section, the most important one, eventually reached a depth of 350 fathoms below adit, and had two sub-vertical shafts, the Old and the New Submarine Shafts. The first was some 1,300 ft. to seaward and the second a similar distance beyond it. They connected the 210 and 302 fathom levels and the 260 and the 350 fathom levels respectively, and both were vertical. The Old Submarine Shaft was provided with a steam winding-engine and boiler in a man-made cavern. It worked despite the heat and smoke. The New Submarine Shaft was provided in 1897 with a compressed air winding-engine.

At surface a great variety of machinery not connected with the work of the shafts was accumulated over the years, in addition to the dressing plant. In the north-eastern part of the mine was the 32-inch stamping-engine. Only its boiler chimney remains. In 1906 it was made double-acting and its power improved. By 1909 there was a battery of 96 heads of stamps, of which 76 were Cornish and 20 Californian. In a north-westerly wind the roar of the stamps could be heard in Penzance. Indeed, the noise of stamps, large and small, is now a long-lost feature of Cornish life. Probably the hearers only noticed when the noise ceased.

The problem of hauling trucks up an incline from the vicinity of the Skip Shaft and bringing ore to the stamps was solved in a way typical of Cornish mining. A drive was taken for the winder off the end of the stamps drive. Cornish mining engineering was distinguished for three features, firstly brilliant innovation (as the career of Richard Trevithick shows), secondly ingenious improvisation, and thirdly (it must be admitted) what was known in Cornwall as a "lash-up", a phrase still in use to mean a dubious expedient. The print of Levant machinery in what must have been the days of the old company shows something like a lash-up in some of its features. The hard-worked stamps engine did yet a third duty; it pumped water from the adit for the processing plant.

The processing of copper was relatively simple. It was broken up and the waste disposed of by men and bal maidens using hammers. Then it was jigged in a sieve in water, the copper going to the bottom. Tin and mixed ores proved more complicated and bring us to a large area adjacent to the stamps. Here took place four processes, buddling, calcining, kieving and leaching. The milling processes of the mine were modified over the years to meet the variations in the compositions of the ore-bodies.

The following methods are indicative and are basic to the general treatment processes. Light drags of cloth, or other material, such as leather, fixed on revolving arms circled the buddles. (Buddles can still be seen at Levant and Botallack). Power came from a water-wheel, a favourite source of cheap power on Cornish mines. The buddles look like upturned soup plates, about 8 ft in diameter, with a surround about 24 ft in diameter. The purpose of the revolving arms with their drags was to distribute evenly the slime so that the minerals would arrange themselves according to their different specific gravities. Cassiterite (tin oxide), being the heaviest, would settle at the head of the buddle. Then following outwards would be the copper, zinc, iron and arsenic sulphides, until furthest out would be the lightest of all, quartz, as a tailing. The fine slime containing tin oxide went to settlement, where after settling it was dug out, then concentrated in concave buddles and rag frames.

The sulphides, and tin oxides, were calcined in Brunton reverbatory [sic] furnaces, to convert the sulphides into oxides. The arsenic oxide was condensed in a flue labyrinth, known as 'The Cathedral' at Levant. Unfortunately it has disappeared, along with much else at the mine site. But a fine example can be seen at Botallack about a mile along the coast. The arsenic was sent to Penzance Station, by horse and cart, and despatched for refining.

There does not seem to have been overmuch concern over the health of the workers or the public; except that the fumes were dispersed by a tall chimney. The other oxides were further buddled. Copper oxide was treated with sulphuric acid in leaching tanks to produce copper sulphate. The copper was precipitated from the solution by scrap iron.

The remaining iron oxide was removed by a magnetic separator. In the case of tin oxide there was a kieving in the tin yard to produce a good commercial quality concentrate ready for bagging and sale. For a long period the smelter was Bolitho's at the east end of Penzance, in Chyandour. The Bolithos were prominent adventurers in Levant (and many other mines) and the black tin was sold on contract to them. Whether this was a favourable arrangement for the mine is arguable.

In 1895 a successful underground telephone system was installed by Valentine Corin, AMIEE, of the Anchor Foundry, Penzance. In 1898 a new form of power arrived, a 6-h.p. Hornsby oil engine, replacing the water power used for the buddles and calciners. It was a big change from the four 20-foot water-wheels employed in 1842.

Meanwhile, in 1880 the first compressed air drill had appeared, with a Harvey compressor at the rear of the pumping-engine house. At first compressed air drills were not generally issued to miners for driving and stoping. Though their advantages were obvious they were initially used on a very small scale, for in the St Just district the lodes are typically narrow as compared with tin and copper lodes in other parts of the county, and on very narrow lodes it was common (and easier) for a man to work single-handed with a borer if no country rock was to be removed.

Levant about 1840, showing features which seem to match the description of a "lash-up".
Drawn and etched by A. M. Scobell of Poltair, Madron, Penzance

Rack or rag frames in the concentrating yard, 1930.

Russell Bayles

A rather inaccurate drawing of the man engine surface plant.

Royal Institution of Cornwall

The tall stack of the compressor house; little else survives from this 1930 photo. On the left the dry with the boiler house behind.

Russell Bayles

The Higher Bal section, formerly part of Spearne Consols Mine. *Copyright Trounson-Bullen Collection*

Miners at Levant with candles stuck on their hardened felt hats with clay.

Jack Corin Collection

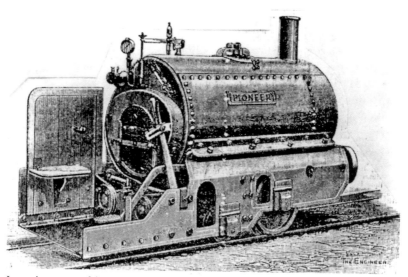

Levant's unsuccessful underground steam loco.   *Eric Edmonds Collection*

One half of the great battery of Cornish stamps at Levant. On the extreme right can be seen the gear wheel taking the power for hauling trams up the incline from the ore sorting floor.   *Copyright Trounson-Bullen Collection*

A pit pony at work tramming on the 278-fathom level.

Copyright Trounson-Bullen Collection

The building which housed the Californian stamps battery.

Russell Bayles

In Levant the men said that they could do a third more work with a higher air-pressure. So the management launched forth on the matter and built a splendid new compressor house. Only a fragment of it remains, beside its very tall chimney with decorative bands and 1901 date stone. The new engine was a large horizontal triple-expansion model designed by George Eustice and Nicholas Trestrail. Its 18-foot diameter 20-ton flywheel must have been impressive in action. It supplied air to the drills under ground and also to the air hoist at New Submarine Shaft. After 1919 the engine was replaced by a Belliss & Morcom 750 cu. ft. air compressor. At about the same time two 170-kilowatt steam electric generators were installed. It was the sort of plant which had almost become standard equipment on the larger Cornish mines during the so-called electric pump boom of the 1900s, and involved a considerable outlay. The power station at Hayle had been built as far back as 1906, mainly to supply Hayle and the towns and mines of Camborne and Redruth. It may appear to have been a wrong decision of the management to have installed its own generating plant but the decision seemed sound at the time as there had been no promise of a reliable public supply.

Levant's equipment in the nineteenth century was not restricted to fixed plant and power drills. It also acquired a steam-locomotive. The 278 fathom level was the main tramming level of the mine, and it was thought that a small industrial locomotive by Bickle of Plymouth could perform the job better than hand-tramming. The 278 was enlarged to 5ft by 5ft to take it. It was by no means a specialised machine which could consume its own smoke as existed up country. But the decision-makers would not have to put up with the heat and smoke. The locomotive was a failure, however, having insufficient adhesion to haul trams of ore on the wet rails in the 278. So shortly after its trial in 1892 it was replaced by pit ponies, and the 278 was renamed the Pony Level. This was a sad admission of defeat in a county where Trevithick invented the steam locomotive, the "mobile power pack of the Industrial Revolution". In view of the difficulties of getting men and machinery under ground in Levant it may well be asked how the ponies fared. The answer was in a sling with legs tied together down the Skip Shaft. The R.S.P.C.A. did not catch up with this.

Road steam locomotives (traction engines), by contrast, were successful, and by 1896 the mine had two in service. What the people of Penzance thought of them as they rumbled through the streets with their trucks is not recorded. The other St Just mines had no alternative to the horse and cart for taking mine produce to Penzance and bringing back machinery, as well as coal to feed the ever-hungry mine boilers. Somehow they contended with Trig-the-Wheel Hill, a long gradient on the St Just side of Newbridge, and this must have been something of a struggle even for the traction engines.

It is difficult to assess what (if any) form of transport the mine had when the old company began work about 1819. It is recorded that in 1760 there was not a road in Penzance fit for wheeled traffic. At the beginning of the next century wheeled vehicles were rare west of the town, and there is evidence to show that at least the small mines were still using pack mules and horses. Farmers might have had something between a wheelbarrow and a cart, with three solid wheels. The lack of expertise in making wheels was displayed in recent times by the customary Cornish wheelbarrow with a solid wheel.

The old company at Levant must have had its machinery delivered by wheeled transport. As the machinery became antiquated the company was reluctant to incur the cost of new machinery, with further problems of transport and delivery cost. Moreover, there was a slump in copper prices in the 1860s, and the general worsening of the company's position led to its reorganisation in 1870. This was effected by a provisional committee consisting of Messrs. Coombs, Carr and Bergtheil of London and J. B. Coulson, a Penzance timber and coal merchant, in 2,000 shares, increased in 1875 to 2,500.

LORDS, CAPTAINS and ADVENTURERS

Levant at that time (1882) was notoriously ill run, being described on one occasion as "a dockyard affair".

Cyril Noall, Geevor

CHAPTER FOUR

The coup de grâce for the old company was its failure to agree with the mineral lords on the terms for a renewal of the lease. The ownership of mineral rights (other than those of hydrocarbons) had become very complicated down the years due to the disposal of land. Freeholds were sold, but the new owners only acquired the surface, and the minerals beneath were reserved by the vendors, who might sell them, or only a fraction of them, to third parties, or divide them amongst their children. For example, the acreage of mineral rights now held by the Duchy of Cornwall is far in excess of its surface land. The Levant company, like any other mining company, was obliged to negotiate with its mineral lords before it could renew its lease, and the lords were free to impose conditions for the development and working of the mine under each renewal.

However, the new company took over and gave Levant a new lease of life, both in a metaphorical and literal sense, after agreement with the lords. Two problems had to be faced in its first decade: the renewal of much of the machinery and the slump in the price of tin. There had been increasing overseas production of copper in the preceding half-century, mitigated by fiscal juggling on imports of copper by the government. But strong overseas over-production of tin hit Levant hard, since it like numerous other Cornish mines had been turning from copper to tin in depth. True there had been booms and slumps in the tin price from the Middle Ages onwards, but overproduction in Australia and the Far East in the 1870s caused another slump in the metal prices of even greater proportions than its predecessors.

The old company, as it became known, had scarcely managed to drag the mine from the eighteenth century into the nineteenth. For the rest of the latter the new company brought the company into about the middle of the nineteenth century. In the twentieth century it remained largely in the nineteenth. The new company could not look forward to the sort of benefits the old company had enjoyed, even if the values of tin under the sea were good. The mine went on with financial results which were only fair as a rule, and Levant became something of an institution with modest rather than highly successful results. There were plenty of ore reserves, but the prosperity of the mine depended on a variety of men in various roles, just like any other business. As we have seen, there were the adventurers, the committee of management, the office staff, the captains, and the miners.

There was no identifiable chief engineer in charge of the machinery, and for many years the mine relied on the experience of practical men and an occasional visit from a consultant. Still less was there a mining engineer as general manager, since men with formal qualifications only began to come along in the county with the establishment of local mining classes in the 1860s, followed by mining schools towards the end of the century. There was, however, a managing agent. Agent was a confusing term applied to the captains, whether managers or under-managers. The title of captain is thought to have been introduced by the German miners invited to assist in the development of mining in Cornwall in the sixteenth century, since they had a hierarchical system of management using military titles. In Cornwall, although the title of captain was respected as much in mining as in maritime affairs, it could be (and still is) applied to farmers and other employers and educated people. It can even be used somewhat opprobriously to anyone, in the sense of "Now look 'ere ole cap'un . . ."; just the difference in deference between the Cornish and the German.

The Cornish captains were practical men promoted from the ranks of the working miners. There were two categories of miner, the tributers and the tutworkers. The latter worked on non-productive but necessary tasks under ground, at a fixed price per fathom. The tributers were in the nature of sub-contractors. The "takers" or foremen of each "pare" or gang would bid for a pitch in the mine at monthly setting days, to be paid at so much in the pound for the payable ore they sent to surface or "grass". Those who had an eye on bidding for a pitch next to the one they had worked would often go to some lengths to conceal its true value. But the captains had been brought up in the same school and knew all the tricks of the trade, so the contest tended to be an even one.

The captains were in effect the middle management of the mine, and on them its smooth working depended, not only in the work under ground, but also in the handling and maintenance of machinery, the supervising of the dressing floors, the pitwork in the shafts and the supply of mine stores. In addition there were ancillary workers, engine-men who drove the engines, blacksmiths with a steam-hammer in their shop who even made the bal nails, and carpenters or binders, who did the timber-work. They were all expert men, or they did not hold their jobs, but some degree of supervision and organisation was required for them. There survives a set of twenty-three verses mentioning all the twenty-nine captains at Levant by name, a marvellous number of them. The final verse concluded: Too many Cappens/By the one half.

The managing agent, whose role can be said to have survived into recent times as the captain of the mine, reported to the purser in the count house or mine office. Levant's count-house was a double-fronted building in the area up behind the pumping-engine house. It was provided with bay windows to which the men could come for their pay. It was fronted with granite ashlar, and along with the majority of the mine's buildings was demolished after the mine closed. But it was reincarnated in a house in Marazion. Its granite steps grace the end of a semi-detached house in Tolver Place, Penzance, formerly the residence of Bill Harry, Raymond Harry's brother.

Within the count-house were the mine officials. In the old company Richard White was clerk from 1850, resident clerk from 1861, and assisted by James Rowe. He was appointed purser to the new company in 1872. He rose to become an Honorary Major of the 1st Volunteer Battalion of the Duke of Cornwall's Light Infantry, which gave him considerable social status, and he became known to all as Major Dick White, one of the great characters of Cornish Mining, in a day when the industry held many characters. The last great character in the industry was the late Jack Trounson, President of the Trevithick Society, who died in 1987. He attempted to revive the mine when it closed in 1930 and was one of those instrumental in saving the whim engine (see chapter 9). Major White is credited with managing the mine through the crisis of the 1870s when the machinery was antiquated and there was a crisis in the price of tin. He remained a key figure until his death in 1909 and it may be said that he was Levant.

Major White contrived to be purser of numerous other mines at various times, small enterprises, but one was near Helston. He was also Chairman of the local Council, a County Councillor and a JP. It could not have left him much time to command No. 1 Company of the 1st Volunteer Battalion of the Duke of Cornwall's Light Infantry. White's career was somewhat marred in 1893 by a great quarrel

LEVANT MINE.

Statement of Accounts for 16 Weeks, ending January 2nd, 1904.

1903—4. Dr. To Labour Cost.	£ s. d.		1903—4. Cr. By Tin Sales.—Consolidated Tin Smelting Co. Ltd., Williams, Harvey, & Co., and Cornish Tin Smelting Co.		£ s. d
Oct. 17. 4 weeks ending Oct. 10 £2629 0 5					
Nov. 14. 4 do. „ Nov. 7 2403 7 10				T. c. q. lb £ s. d. £ s. d.	
Dec. 12. 4 do. „ Dec. 5 2417 17 2			Oct. 30, 20 0 2 0 @ 77 2 6 1544 8 6		
Jan. 9. 4 do. „ Jan. 2 2507 11 3			„ „ 20 0 1 17 @ 77 7 6 1549 1 0		
Surgeon and Club Payments ... 101 0 10			Nov. 25, 10 0 0 22 @ 76 10 0 765 15 0		
	10058 17 6		„ 27, 10 0 0 0 @ 76 10 0 765 0 0		
To Tribute on Leavings—Tin and Copper......	164 9 2		„ „ 20 0 1 1 @ 76 17 6 1538 9 10		
„ Merchants' Bills	2798 18 8		Dec. 22, 2 1 1 15 @ 72 0 0 148 19 8		
„ Harvey & Co. on A/c. Timber (Cargo)......	350 0 0		„ „ 1 15 2 11 @ 71 15 0 127 14 2		
„ Workmen's Compensation — Additional			„ 23, 10 0 2 6 @ 83 5 0 834 16 0		
Premium	1 0 0		„ 28, 20 0 0 0 @ 83 2 6 1662 10 0		
„ Coals ex ship	1340 3 10		„ „ 9 19 2 8 @ 83 5 0 830 14 3		
„ Harvey & Co., Traction Carriage and Wharfage :			Jan. 22, 20 0 0 0 @ 82 2 6 1642 10 0		
Coal............. £100 4 8			„ „ 19 19 1 21 @ 81 2 6 1620 4 4		
Copper 87 14 7					13030 2 9
	187 19 3		163 17 3 17		
„ Rents	64 4 5		By Tin Leavings :—		
„ Bankers' Interest and Discount on Drafts	100 2 10		Nov. 28, 2 3 0 26 @ 57 0 0 123 4 3		
	15,065 15 8		Jan. 22, 1 19 2 20 @ 56 10 0 112 1 10		
			4 2 3 18		235 6 1
					13,265 8 10
			168 0 3 7		
„ Lords' Dues	664 0 1		By Copper Sales :—		
	15,729 15 9		Nov. 5, 265T. 0c. 3q. £1574 11 8		
			Dec. 31, 363T. 2c. 3q. 1288 18 2		2863 9 10
„ Balance, Profit on this Account	735 1 1		628T. 3c. 2q.		
			By Carriage of Copper Ore 208 17 3		
			„ „ Tin 4 10 0		213 7 3
			„ Workmen's Compensation Claims allowed......		24 7 0
			„ Sundries		56 10 2
			„ Discount on Merchants' Bills		41 13 9
£16,464 16 10					£16,464 16 10

1903. Oct. 6.—To Dividend made at 5/- per Share on 2385 Shares	£ s. d. 596 5 0		By Balance in favour of Adventurers at last A/c 1617 1 4		£ s. d.
To Balance now in favour of the Adventurers	1755 17 5		„ Profit on this Account as above		735 1 1
	£2,352 2 5				£2,352 2 5

GENERAL BALANCE SHEET.

LIABILITIES.	£ s. d.		ASSETS.	£ s. d.
To Bills unpaid	3302 3 9		By Copper Ore Sold, and Carriage	4091 16 2
„ Lords' Dues	704 2 4		„ Arsenic	1279 4 10
„ Cheques Outstanding	677 13 8		„ Subsist Advanced, &c.	50 0 0
„ Cost Book Balance	1755 17 5		„ Balance in favour of Mine at Bank	962 6 10
„ Dividends unpaid.............................	55 12 6		„ Bills receivable	112 1 10
	£6,495 9 8			£6,495 9 8

January 23rd, 1904.

Examined and found correct,
JOHN DOIDGE, *Auditor.*

RICHARD WHITE, *Purser.*

	T. c. q. lb.	£ s. d.
Tin Stuff Stamped	6997T. 1c. 0qr. 3lbs.	
Copper Ore Sold :—Burnt	19T. 11c. 0qr.	78 13 11
Rough	424T. 19c. 0qr.	2386 13 8
Precipitate	11T. 15c. 2qr.	398 2 3
	628T. 3c. 2qr.	£2863 9 10

with Captain Trezise, who had been managing agent and had made a considerable contribution to the revival of the mine by the new company. After a row in the adventurers' committee the unfortunate Trezise was dismissed and White remained supreme until his death in 1909.

Not only was he the top executive but later also Chairman with an eighth share in the mine. His house was in Trewellard. How he travelled to the mine in those days did not prevent him from appearing

18

immaculate in topper and frock coat, as the frontispiece shows.

Above the Major was the committee of management, whose members were drawn from among the adventurers. Among them were two comedians, Dr Quick and Dr Searle. They were not quite so pressed in their duties in those days as modern general practitioners. Certainly the former found time to be purser of a mine called Wheal Bal on the hill of the same name leading up from Trewellard to the North Road. He worked it as Wheal Do'em and got it into production on an outlay of £100. Searle was the only qualified doctor of the two, and was surgeon and medical officer for the Penzance Union, St Just District. Both gentlemen were noted for their quips, jokes and pertinent remarks at the periodical meetings. It is quite useful to have a committee member who can lessen tension at some crisis with an amusing comment, but one is enough! Quick was a member of the committee from 1873 to 1893, but Searle was not.

A typical remark by Dr Searle at a meeting of the adventurers in 1883 was that the alleged bad management of the mine could be cured by advising the adventurers to "cut off the supply of grog, and you will dissolve the committee at once." Dr Quick, among innumerable recorded remarks at various times, said, when a loss was reported and when asked in jocular style what dividend he would recommend, said "Where are you going to get it from? You will have to go to the Devil for your dividend!" This brought a roar of laughter. Dr Searle's comment on the bad management in Levant and other mines in Cornwall was that for up-country investors they had produced an "Aceldama to bury strangers in". This assumed that other members of the committee were familiar with Acts I 19. The Oxford English Dictionary says Aceldama was the field near Jerusalem bought with the blood money received by Judas Iscariot, hence, figuratively, a field of bloodshed.

By contrast, the most far-seeing committee member was Francis (Frank) Oats. He was remarkable in becoming a qualified man in mining as early as 1866, when he passed first class in the examination in Mineralogy (inter alia) of the Science and Art Department at South Kensington, tying nationally for

Visitors outside the count house. On the right, miners with bunches of candles. The figure in dark suit and white jacket is, as a guess, Captain Ben Nicholas, a notable Levant character.

Penlee House Museum

first place. In 1871 he became a captain at Botallack Mine, and three years later went as Inspector to the diamond fields in South Africa, where he spent two years. He ultimately became chairman of De Beers Consolidated Mines, Basset Mines and Levant, in all of which he had large shareholdings, and a member of the Cape Parliament. By the values of his times he was a millionaire. Were it not for the fact that he spent half the year in South Africa he might have exercised more influence, for with experience of modern mining in South Africa he could see that Levant was a living museum of Cornish mining. But "dear old Major", after half a century, could not but have been a very restraining influence.

At the periodical meetings the purser presented the accounts. If the results were good the adventurers were given a good dinner, if bad they were given a good dinner to cheer them up. Grog was served, hence Dr Searle's comment. One purser's reply to the question why the cost of the spirits did not appear in the accounts replied "Well, they're there, but you can't see them!" In accordance with Parkinson's second law the drinks bill could prove an important topic. In the February 1892 account it was £9 4s 6d, and one must remember that money was then worth about 32 times what it is today. But no doubt drink was cheaper in real terms then. One adventurer described the figure as an "improvement". Nevertheless, the adventurers did not notably abstain from drinking the grog. The floor of the dining-room in the Levant count-house showed burn marks where guests, slumped back in their chairs, had allowed lighted cigars to drop from their fingers. One good cause of this was Major White's famous punch. Actually it was an old Dorset recipe, not a Cornish one, but nobody minded that. It was composed of:

> One bottle Jamaica rum
> Half bottle Cognac
> One tumbler lemon juice
> A dash of Benedictine
> Two pounds of sugar
> One whole lemon rind in the piece.

20

Put the sugar, lemon juice and rind in a gallon container. Add cognac and rum. Pour on boiling water from a height (to oxygenise it).

The result is expensive but highly recommended. On social occasions the Trevithick Society uses the recipe, reduced in strength for those who must remain sober. According to the late Jack Trounson, himself an abstainer, "Major White's particular brew of punch was so potent that the smell of it a quarter of a mile away would knock any man blind drunk." Allowing for a degree of hyperbole in this statement it was certainly as strong a brew as in the Navy. The word purser was pronounced "pusser" locally (it still is in the Navy), and "Pusser's Rum" in the Navy was very potent. Some ratings who had "sippers round the Mess" on their birthday were inclined to die of alcoholic poisoning. The daily ration to junior ratings was one and a half gills of water to half a gill of rum. How the Levant adventurers got home on horseback or driving a trap after a count-house dinner one can only speculate. The horses probably knew the way, and they feared not the breathalyser!

The late Dr. A. K. Hamilton Jenkin attended one of the very last of the count-house dinners, at a mine in St Agnes parish. He recalled how the count-house women came in from the kitchen bearing great steaming joints of beef. As the doors opened there came into the room the roar of the stamps. Those old-fashioned days are long gone, as is, sadly, nearly every working mine in Cornwall.

According to the verses about Levant's "Cappens" had two count-house women; we should call them ladies now:

> Then next comes Cappen Fanny
> And also Cappen Grace;
> Among the other Cappens
> They too must have their place.
> They cook the beef and mutton
> And serve the bread and cheese,
> They do not care a button
> Whether they vex or please.

Perhaps South Crofty in Camborne was the last mine to have a count-house woman. If one went as a visitor as late as about 1950 the routine was to take along one of mother's pasties. It would be larger and infinitely superior to the machine-made objects retailed in these latter days, which demean the county's tradition. On arrival the pasty was handed to the count-house woman. On return to the count-house after inspecting the mine underground and the ore dressing floors the pasty would be removed from the oven of the Cornish range where it had been put to warm, while one endeavoured to remove the red water marks from one's clothes and person.

There was a distinct reflection of count-house dinners in Geevor's latter years, when the annual general meeting of shareholders was held on the mine, at first in the board-room and later in the Sports Club. A buffet lunch was provided and long service awards were presented to miners, a distinctly modern custom.

In Cornish mines when a new engine, usually a pumping-engine, was put to work, there was often a celebration for all. The nearest and perhaps the only time Levant approached to such a festival was in August 1872, when a new 45-inch Harvey pumping engine replaced the worn-out 40-inch. Then, between fifty and sixty workmen, who had been engaged in the engine's erection, sat down to a celebration dinner presided over by Major White. By contrast, Wheal Busy, near Chacewater, celebrated the installation of two new pumping-engines with an ox-roast for all hands.

THE MEN and WOMEN of LEVANT

Those who are not killed by accident perish of exhaustion and excessive toil; the rock is hard and the ladders are so long. Very admirable is the stoical coldness with which they regard their fate. Cornwall is proud, and justly so, of her miners. Who can say what England owes to these men? They produce riches, and scarcely enjoy common necessaries themselves.

Alphonse Esquiros, Cornwall and its Coasts, 1865.

CHAPTER FIVE

Most historians of mines or groups of mines in Cornwall tend to concentrate on geology, engineering, or economic history. Little attention is paid by them to the men who did the work, or the women and girls on the surface, let alone the boys who toiled above and below ground from an early age. The great exception is the late Dr A. K. Hamilton Jenkin, whose classic *The Cornish Miner* was published in 1927 and subsequently reprinted several times. He covered almost every aspect of the miner's life from early times, and had the advantage of knowing men who had worked in the previous century. But even he said little about the female workers, the bal-maidens, as they were called, and we have to rely on essayists like George Henderson or outsiders like J. R. Leifchild. Other occasional travellers in Cornwall have added their comments, not least the Portuguese Alphonse Esquiros and a Manchester clergyman, Rev. F. J. Horsefield. The latter stayed at Pendeen vicarage a century ago. He visited Levant and observed the local scene. He was a very keen observer and must have made very careful notes on his visit to the mine, for he describes what he saw in some detail.

Cornish miners were not apt to write their autobiographies, although some wrote verses and Thomas Merritt, an Illogan miner, composed tunes for carols which are still sung in Cornwall with enthusiasm. Levant had no composers, but an excellent writer in the late Raymond Harry of Carnyorth. In 1917 he went to work in Levant at the age of fourteen, and in 1962 he published a book called The Mine Under the Sea, under the pen-name of Jack Penhale. His accounts of various phases of his life in Levant would shame many who leave school at sixteen today, and some of the incidents he records would horrify an Inspector of Mines. He details working conditions in the mine in the twentieth century. We can be sure that they were as bad and worse in the previous century. For much of its life-span Levant had five or six hundred employees, men, women and children.

Apart from individual dangers there are three ever-present threats to health and safety in a mine, namely temperature, ventilation, and climbing ladders. The Trevithick Society party working on the restoration of the winding-engine were given an underground tour of Levant in October 1990. At that time Geevor was only running its upcast fan on a night tariff, so we may assume that the temperature of up to 82°F which the party recorded would have been typical of the mine when it was working. The humidity was very high. One member of the party weighed himself before he left home and found after the four-hour trip that he had lost 7 lbs. This was the same as the weight loss of a miner on a Levant shift, and he was probably ill-nourished by present standards. One, Henry Maddern, recalled that the 326 and 314 were the hottest levels and "would fill your boots with sweat." In 1842, when the mine was not so deep a captain averred that even a six-hour shift would "work a man down".

Allied to the subject of temperature was the matter of ventilation in the mine. The effects of blasting added to the problem, as did the use of the steam-engine in Old Submarine Shaft, to say nothing of the underground locomotive. It has been questioned whether the smoke or "smeach" it produced led to its withdrawal rather than the slippery rails. Metalliferous mines are always more difficult to ventilate than coal mines with a more regular layout. In the case of Levant a large portion of the mine being under the sea compounded the difficulty. Under the land air-shafts could be used. Under the sea there were several answers. Winzes were sunk between the levels and stulls or screens were used to direct the draught from the air machines employed. The latter were fans turned by a wretched boy on a six to eight hour shift. Later, compressed air was sent down through pipes. The eventual solution, when the mine acquired large compressors, was to send compressed air down. This was applied in the 326, known as "Little Hell". It was said that there was hardly enough air there to keep a candle alight, but that the lode was "rich as a Jew's box". Smoking twist would hardly have improved the atmosphere.

The danger of an accumulation of radon gas in a mine where ventilation is poor was not recognised until about twenty or more years ago. But Cornish miners in the last century may not have lived long enough to be affected by its alleged carcinogenic qualities. There was little silicosis, because most of the mine was in the killas rather than in granite. But many Levant men went to the hot, dry mines of the Rand before water to keep down the dust was introduced into the drill shafts. They earned good money but shortened their lives.

Cornish miners suffered more from pulmonary diseases through climbing ladders in shafts. Levant miners were spared this by the introduction of the man-engine. They also had the benefit of a changing-house. One was burnt down in 1859, and the one which lasted until the mine closed was built in 1888. It was 70 ft long and 14 ft wide, well-lighted, and a stream of water flowed through for the men to wash in while their clothes were dried on steam pipes. Only the floor with four sunken baths survives. In 1899 it was joined by a flight of spiral stone steps to the head of the Man Engine Shaft via a tunnel. This meant that men coming up did not have to face the weather before they had changed into their outdoor clothes.

Workers on the surface, men, women and boys, had obviously a rather healthier life than the miners underground, but the distinction was only relative. Victorian writers tended to exaggerate the virtues of working in the open air. The workers were more hardy than present-day people, because they were used to the open air and had but little heating at home. Survivors of shipwrecks would live all night in conditions which would kill the average present-day human in an hour or less. The Reverend Horsefield wrote: "The floors on which the bal-maidens work are kept beautifully clean, and the work is performed in sweet pure air. The happiness of sunshine is around the people, and brightens their lives." In fact, fog is prevalent in the St Just-Pendeen area, and not only in winter. It has a micro-climate which can produce persistent fog in summer when the sun is shining only a mile or two away. It is said that the people of St Just never minded working underground because they never saw the sun anyway! The Trevithick Society workers on the restoration of the whim engine at Levant will testify to the incidence of rain, wind and fog. In the winter, when it was not one of the three, it was often all three together. The surface workers at Levant must often have had their own thoughts about working in the "sweet pure air", since waterproof clothing was hardly known to them.

For those on the surface there were dangers from the machinery, but at least they could see them. For the men underground there were always hidden dangers, not only those concealed in rock which might fall. The standard illumination was by a tallow candle. The miners wore hard felt hats and on them were stuck the candles in a lump of clay. There could hardly have been a cruder method. Even the illumination from a modern miner's electric lamp seems to the layman underground only just adequate, and it is hard to imagine how one coped by the light of a candle. It was not until 1927 that Levant progressed to carbide lamps, which had been introduced in other Cornish mines over twenty years earlier.

The present-day preoccupation with health and safety at work was seldom shared by nineteenth century employers, even though a mine's General Articles, which included rudimentary safety precautions, were read out to the miners at regular intervals. Blasting was a particular hazard, using quills or reeds filled with black powder for a fuse. In 1831 John Solomon Bickford invented the safety fuse, a great gift to miners all over the world. Until then the sight of a maimed or blind miner, hurt in a blasting accident, was all too common in the mining districts of Cornwall. Indeed, in St Just it may have continued longer, for in the 1920s the late A. K. Hamilton Jenkin met miners in west Cornwall who had used black powder throughout their working lives. Herbert Thomas, a noted mining journalist a century ago, cheerfully remarked that "dynamite either kills or does not hurt." Levant men raised to an art the biting of the cap on the detonator to secure it to the end of the fuse. A slight error in this process, instead of using the special pliers provided, would have led to death. Levant's little detonator store survives in ruined condition, a short distance south-west along the cliff from the whim-engine house.

During his time as a young man in Levant in the first quarter of the century Raymond Harry describes a particularly dangerous maintenance job he and three others undertook at the end of the 278. They had to repair the launders there, from which water was leaking into the stopes below. It was known that the place was dangerous because of rotting timbers and loose heavy ground in imminent danger of collapse. On the way the danger signs were all too evident, and they negotiated a large hole spanned by an eight-inch wide plank with the help of the timber they were carrying with them. No Inspector of Mines would have allowed them to go on this trip: any loud noise or false step could have meant disaster. The return journey was even more hazardous as they had nothing with which to supplement the eight-inch plank. They arrived at the shaft in safety, pursued to within an inch of their lives by a cave-in or "run of ground" heard throughout the mine. Such was a day in the life of a Levant miner!

That was not the only alarming and out of the ordinary experience which Harry experienced when in Levant. On one occasion he and his workmate were asked to find where the rising main in the pumping engine shaft had burst somewhere above the 278. They set off up the ill-maintained ladders of the Engine Shaft, not even by the light of tallow candles, for they were doused by the water coming down. In the ascent they are in constant danger from the plunging pump rods, thin or missing rungs on the ladders, and slippery sollars at various stages. Only his workmate's splendid memory of the difficulties of the shaft saved Harry. After ascending a ladder which hangs slightly backwards they came to the 40 fathom level where the burst of the pipe had occurred, not, as the Captain on the surface thought, low down not far from the 278. Having made a temporary repair they ascended to the adit level and climbed 250 feet up the cliff path to meet the Captain in the pumping engine house. He was astonished at their feat in climbing the shaft so far in the face of a deluge of water. He accepted that the two men have had enough for one day and were going to change and go home!

It was not an everyday experience but indicative of the trials that a miner was prepared to undertake in the service of the mine. Even in Geevor's latter days men were more prepared to undertake a dangerous task than modern management was prepared to allow them.

Having survived the shift without mishap the Levant miner spent up to half an hour ascending the man engine to the comforts of the dry. On emerging from it in his dry clothes he faced a walk home. That could be several miles, perhaps over rough cliff paths, pleasant enough for a summer stroll but not so in the dark of winter in the wind and rain. If we take as a random sample the unfortunate 31 men who died in the man engine disaster we find that 17 of them lived in St. Just, two miles away as the crow flies. By the shortest road route it was three miles and there was no public transport, even if it could have been afforded. One wonders to what extent miners ever used bicycles.

Miners' pay was based on the price the mine received for its ores, standard prices for both copper and tin being notified to the men at the beginning of a contract. An early record was made in 1837 by Sir Charles Lemon for the Journal of the Statistical Society, which was reprinted in De la Beche's geological survey of 1839. The wage rates in mines west of Penzance were then the lowest in the county. Tributers received 47s 6d per month, tutworkers 45s and labourers 42s. Mine workers were paid on a four or five-week month and not a 52-week year. In June 1881, with a high tin standard, pay at Levant was the best for twenty years, with tributers receiving £5 4s 6d and tutworkers £3 18s 8d. Two years later, with a lower metal price, underground men were receiving £3 15s a month, boys £1 0s 2d, surface men £3 and surface boys 10s. Individual tributers might have a good "sturt" or rich strike in one or two months; for instance, in 1874 two tributers on a two-month contract in the 210 cut a rich bunch of ore and received £40 each for eight weeks' work. But in general wages remained low; with a low tin standard the average at Levant in 1893 was £3 a month, never more than £4, while bal-maidens received 5s and girls 3s 6d a week. At about this time C. V. Thomas, the lawyer member of an eminent Camborne mining family, was moved to remark "When miners are paid better we can expect them to work fifty hours a week instead of thirty or thirty-five as at present." One can hardly believe he was speaking seriously!

By 1910 Levant men were earning £4 15s a month underground, and good men could earn £6 to £7 15s. In Raymond Harry's time pay had risen to £6 a month, compared to £100 to £120 on the Rand. It is worth remembering that as late as 1939 a labourer's wage in Penzance was only 30s a week. Because monthly wages were inconvenient for miners, it became the custom for pursers to make advances of pay or earnings weekly or fortnightly. These were known as subsist or "'sist", and were accounted for at the end of the contract, when the taker or each gang of men received an account and a cash payment of any balance due to him and his mates. Mine managements frequently charged for candles at a price slightly above those charged in the local shops, in order to discourage miners from selling them and taking unnecessary risks with insufficient light under ground. The cost of candles was charged to both tributers and tutworkers, as were pick hilts, tools, doctor and club, fuse, powder or dynamite, and the mine barber if there was one. Miners were "spaled" or fined for breaking mine regulations or for not completing their bargains, 2s 6d for the first offence and 5s for the second, a considerable sum in those days.

It may have come as a considerable shock to the committee of management of Levant when the Employers' Liability Act was passed in 1881, for it took the mine two years to implement it and to take out the required insurance against accidents involving miners. For many years the men had paid 6d. a month into a sick club, which covered accidents and medical attendance of the mine doctor, Dr Quick, and which extended to sickness at home.

The Education Act of 1870 introduced a basic improvement in the life of children, but it was two years before an Act was passed excluding boys under twelve years of age from working under ground, and limited children's working hours at surface to ten hours a day. In the middle of the nineteenth century there were the beginnings of a move to educate miners for their occupation. A great leader in this was Robert Hunt, F.R.S. (1807-1887), a notable figure in Cornwall. In the 1890s the district mining classes set up by the Miners' Association (of which he was secretary) were consolidated into the Camborne School of Mines, in a granite building in the centre of the town. Among the institutions thus consolidated were the Redruth Mining School, the Camborne Mining School, the School of Arts and Science in Penzance, and the Penzance Mining School, near the Botallack count house, now a dwelling known at Botallack Vean. The Camborne School of Mines subsequently moved to Pool and is now located within the campus of the Combined Universities in Cornwall at Tremough, near Penryn.

Having made his way home with the aid of a candle in a treacle tin (if at night) and perhaps with the aid of his wife out looking for him with a lantern if he came over the cliffs; what sort of home did the man find? The many miners' cottages which survive in rows today look snug and big enough for two people by modern standards. A century and more ago they might only have had an earth floor and be likely to contain a family with several children or young men working at the mine. The bedrooms would have been crowded and the shift system making "hot bunking" a routine, now only spoken of in ocean racing yachts. (But well into this century railwaymen suffered the system in boarding houses of sleeping in a bed another man had vacated.).

Piped water only reached Pendeen in the middle of this century so water would have been drawn from a well for all purposes, and sanitation was of a rudimentary nature. Meanwhile unless good quality granite had been used in the house all too much water would have seeped through the walls.

Count House Day at Levant c1895. Note the boys of school age.

Jack Corin collection.

N. Holman & Sons of St Just are credited with the invention of the Cornish range or "slab" as it was locally known. This succeeded the open fire for cooking, for those who could afford it. The older generation thought that cooking in a slab oven did not taste as well as that on an open fire. In due course another generation favoured the taste of cooking in a slab above that of a gas cooker. St Just had its gas works also run by Holman's. The fire in the slab made the kitchen the usual living room where the only comfort was in hard wooden chairs. At least rents were very low and the miner who had a good sturt might build his own dwelling.

The diet and quality of cooking depended much on the wife a miner had chosen. There was equal opportunity for women in the mining industry — as labourers. Many miners, not surprisingly, married bal maidens. These girls had little time, opportunity, or inclination for acquiring domestic skills, after a day spent breaking copper ore or dressing tin. And if mother had also been a bal maiden they had not the best of tutors. In any case a very limited budget dictated the diet and miners did not suffer from eating too much red meat. It was only seen for the majority on high days and holidays. A cup of tea, perhaps made from mugwort, and a piece of barley bread sent a miner to work, with a hoggan (a baked pastry containing currants or figs and sometimes a piece of pork) for his croust or mid-shift meal. On return his supper would perhaps be salt fish, tow rag, potatoes and mugwort tea. A night cap might be the cold comfort of barley bread, potatoes, and cold water. In such spare time as he had the miner could grow vegetables in his garden, keep a pig (if he could find sufficient to feed it), or even a cow or a half-share in one.

On the Cornish coastline any cove, or even wide cleft in the rocks was sufficient to keep a boat when hunger was the spur. Levant men were fortunate in having Portheras Cove, just beyond Pendeen Lighthouse, and Priest's Cove, under Cape Cornwall, from where they pursued fishing as a spare-time occupation. In the middle of the last century the former even attained the stage of holding a midsummer regatta for lug-sailed craft. Priest's Cove, with surrounding rocks and a swell coming in remains an awkward place to launch a boat. The tradition of part-time fishing was maintained by Geevor men to the end of that mine's life.

In the earlier days of Levant another source of additional income derived from the sea would have been smuggling, or Free Trade as it was politely called in Cornwall. If the miner did not actually go to sea there was money to be earned in the transport of the goods on shore, and for the children to be told to watch the wall while the gentlemen went by was not entirely poetic licence on the part of Kipling.

After the end of the Napoleonic wars the government was able to concentrate on the suppression of smuggling. If you look from Levant towards Pendeen Lighthouse (built 1900) there is a substantial row of white Coastguard cottages, with an observation tower at one end. It shows how seriously smuggling was taken in the district. The Coastguards' prime duty was not life-saving, as now, but maintaining an inshore blockade against the smugglers. To that end a boat was kept in Portheras Cove. We may be sure that not a few miners benefited from involvement in the Trade. To this day old people in West Cornwall refer to spirit beverages as a "drop a Trade".

The miners would also have derived windfalls of goods from the all too frequent wrecks of the nineteenth century. Everything from outright defiance to ingenious circumventions was practised against the Coastguards. It was permissible to salvage cargo as long as it was declared to the Coastguard. Needless to say declaration was made as little as possible. Old habits die hard. A few years ago a container of leaf tobacco came ashore at Pendeen. As a result it was said that the fog siren at Pendeen Watch was sounding not on account of a normal fog but because of a fog of tobacco smoke wafting upwards.

In October 1909 the mine itself was able to take part in salvage but necessarily on a legal basis. The *William Cory* came ashore under Boscaswell Cliff with a cargo of pit props. Levant agreed with the underwriters to salvage as much as possible of the cargo, the mine to receive 50% of its value.

Smuggling came to an end in the last quarter of the nineteenth century for a number of reasons. The blockade became more effective, there were changes in duties, more luxury goods, formerly smuggled, were produced at home and the game became less worth the effort, organisation and finance. Just as important was the influence of Methodism, for Wesley disapproved of smuggling as illegal.

It is no exaggeration to say that the brothers John and Charles Wesley transformed life in Cornwall, even in the remotest parts and among the poorest people. No other individual or organisation has had a greater influence on the spiritual, educational and cultural life of the Cornish people since the early Christian church. Before the coming of Methodism Cornwall might well have been called West Barbary, a name jokingly given to it in 1891 by L. L. Price which was taken from the title of a book published about North Africa in 1671. So poor and neglected were the tinners, miners, labourers and fishermen that they would descend on any wreck and dismantle it. Wreck timber, which was often of very good quality, occasionally found its way into mines to secure the workings.

> From wicked rocks and shelving sands. From Breage and Germoe men's hands.
> Good Lord deliver us.

That little rhyme expresses the mariners' view of Cornish people, intent on what would now be called "recycling" their ships and cargoes. In practice low-church, Methodism civilised the county. Since the Prayer Book Rebellion of the sixteenth century and the resistance to the Reformation it implied, Cornwall has been either neglected by the Church of England or made the recipient of High Church

One of the levels in Levant, photographed J. C. Burrow, a brilliant exponent of underground photography in the nineteenth century. *Copyright Trounson-Bullen Collection.*

The dry. In the foreground is part of the railing around the staircase leading down to the tunnel connecting with the Man Engine Shaft. *Copyright Trounson-Bullen Collection*

parsons. The western parishes nevertheless maintained their patronal festivals or feasts, and they are celebrated by various events, both religious and lay, to this day. St Just Feast is still marked with considerable gusto!

At first John Wesley met with resistance in his indefatigable preaching. He was capable of delivering six sermons and riding over fifty miles in three days on one tour. When he began to make converts in Cornwall the people responded with enormous enthusiasm. Indeed, Methodism was known as Enthusiasm, but that was because in the eighteenth century the word meant "ill-regulated religious emotion or speculation". As such it was sternly resisted by many in the Church of England. A Bishop of Exeter, in whose Diocese Cornwall then lay, had inscribed on his tombstone *A pious suppressor of Enthusiasm;* and the famous Cornish historian, Reverend William Borlase, who held the living of St Just and Ludgvan in plurality, was a noted opponent of Methodism.

Methodism appealed to the enthusiasm, in the modern sense, of Celtic converts. Many of Charles Wesley's hymns remain firm favourites in the Church of England as well as the Methodist Churches. Song appealed greatly to the Cornish Celts, as it did in Wales. John Wesley himself said "Methodism was born in song" and nowhere was this more true than in Cornwall. The sound of voices filled not only the chapels but the pubs. Out of the chapels were born the male voice choirs, and the ladies' choirs, which are such a feature of present Cornish culture. Sadly, up country landlords have disapproved of singing in pubs and turn up the juke box, not appreciating that singing rules out any trouble. The pilot gig racing clubs maintain the tradition regardless and can usually produce a soloist or two. Once upon a time the singers at the Tinners' Arms in Zennor were the finest singers and when Penzance Pirates XV beat Cardiff the Tinners' Arms men at Zennor beat the Welsh at singing that evening!

Church, Chapel or non-Churchgoers, Levant men had a singing tradition of their own. The shift coming off would sing during their half-hour ascent by the Man Engine. In a BBC2 transmission in 1970 looking back to the man engine disaster a witness, Albert Dymond, described the singing. "They had four male voice choirs here in this district and most of the men worked in the mine and when they travelled the man engine they all started to sing and the sound that you heard as it came up through the shaft was out of this world. If you could stand on the top of that shaft and listen ... rich, it was, rich ... and some never used to believe in church and chapels or anything like that. Yet they would join in the hymns, you know, and everybody with heart and soul in it."

On one occasion the shift coming to work in the afternoon told of a ship in peril off the Land's End, so the mariners' hymn Eternal Father strong to save was sung. The harmonies in the Man Engine Shaft must have been wonderful to hear. Sadly it was all over long before the day of the tape-recorder but what a recording it would have been!

The Non-Conformist lay members of the chapels had to manage their own affairs, without the help of an educated parson, and not least build their own Chapels. St Just has a vast Methodist chapel and there are other smaller chapels scattered around the district, built by miners and others with their own hands. Abandoned mine buildings were sometimes robbed for building stone for the chapels, something which a mining engineer once described as sacrilege! The chapels had their local preachers on the circuits, laymen who somehow acquired an education, but not always a perfect one. Many stories are told of their unconscious humour on occasions, such as the impromptu prayer which began "O Lord, as Thou hast no doubt read in The St Ives Times ..." One at least of Levant's captains, the manager, Captain Ben Nicholas (1871-1926), was a local preacher.

A further benefit of Methodism was its emphasis on abstinence. It did not make the Levant miners into teetotallers. Raymond Harry noted that on Maze Monday, the Monday after pay-day, half the men might be absent through the effects of drink. However, the Reverend Horsefall was able to report in 1893 that he had not seen anyone drunk in the course of ten weeks. Formerly pares of tributers adjourned to the pub to divide their earnings, and there was consequently much drinking, but by the middle of the nineteenth century many miners put their money into saving banks or bought small houses.

So little entertainment was provided that men could hardly be blamed for going to the pubs. The unfortunate bal-maidens were criticised for spending their little money on finery, bought from the packman, "Johnny-come-fortnight", a feature of Cornish life which survived into this century. After breaking copper ore all the week who could grudge them a little diversion?

Cornish miners riding the man engine (at Dolcoath, circa 1892).

Courtesy Royal Institution of Cornwall.

30

It is hard to believe how little entertainment for people there was in a remote area like Pendeen-St Just. The wireless did not arrive until the 1930s and the cinema never came to St Just. Small wonder that annual events like Feast and Church and Chapel treats were looked forward to from one year to another. A visit to Penzance by the St Just horse-bus (traditionally "always room for one more"), if it could be afforded, was a considerable event. Travelling vans brought around domestic items for which there was no local shop and were too bulky to be carried on the bus.

Church or Chapel services, perhaps up to three on a Sunday for children, were an occasion for singing and perhaps a discreet eyeing of the girls. A typical special entertainment was reported by *The Cornishman* newspaper in March 1891. 'PENDEEN. An entertainment has been given in the Pendeen Board-schools by the Cripples Hill choir. Recitation &c were given by members of the Rechabite Society. The Vicar presided. A most enjoyable evening was spent by a goodly audience.' It was probably much better than most modern television programmes!

Foreign travel became popular but only in terms of emigration by the men to find employment in distant mining fields. A St Just girl asked by a stranger whether she had ever been to the Land's End replied, "Naw". The stranger was surprised, but his informant added, "a'course our people have been to South Africy and Australy". It was a St Just miner and a Scillonian who found the famous "Welcome Stranger" gold nugget in Victoria, Australia. It was the biggest single nugget ever discovered in the world, weighing over 200lbs and brought its finders John Deason and Richard Oates, the enormous sum of £9,500 (multiply by 32) more than they might have earned in a lifetime at Levant.

DISASTER

Last, up come Mr Carbis, he said 'My God', he said, 'the man-engine's broke and there's some slaughter down there, T'is some damage done.'

Lionel Ellis, an eye witness, in the BBC2 broadcast of January 1970.

CHAPTER SIX

The prospect of a new century did not seem to have much effect on the imagination of the Levant management. There were but few forward-looking changes in the mine's strategy, if they had but few radical ideas at all. Good values were explored deeper and further under the sea. The New Submarine Shaft and its haulage were completed and the mine was extended down to the 350 fathom level. The greatly increased cost of haulage and handling ore was ignored. By the First World War there were seven separate handlings, at a cost of £2 12s per ton. Higher Bal had been developed, but its contribution to Levant's prosperity was small. Although it was provided with ingenious equipment its ore was carried by horse and cart to the stamps, at some distance down the hill, all adding to production costs. As far as shafts were concerned the crooked Skip Shaft remained as the only hauling shaft. Not only did it draw up ore from the 278, but all stores for underground, such as timber and heavy equipment, had to be sent down it, which led to long delays. This was at a time when other big mines in Cornwall were developing gig haulage for men and materials, a method first introduced at the nearby Botallack Mine in 1863 for the Boscawen Diagonal Shaft. Even Royalty were entrusted to this haulage. On the other hand Levant became the last mine in Cornwall to retain its man-engine the only other one in the British Isles being that at Laxey in the Isle of Man. The consequences for Levant of persisting with the man-engine were to be fatal, not only to 31 men but to numerous injured miners and to the mine's continued existence.

However, in 1895 Levant did in one respect march with the times, and installed telephones underground, only nineteen years after the Scottish emigrant Alexander Graham Bell perfected the first "articulated telephone". Remarkably enough the first mine in Cornwall to have underground telephones was West Wheal Eliza, near St Austell, which tried them out in 1877. With its neighbour Wheal Eliza the mine was run by a Birmingham syndicate and had a go-ahead and highly skilled manager, Richard Harris Williams. But the telephone did not catch on there. Some years later Dolcoath Mine in Camborne tried telephones, but they succumbed to damp and damage to the wires in the shaft caused by the skips. Levant's telephones were supplied by the General Electric Co. and were based on Bell's patents.

The instruments were of gun-metal with a bell carrying a dome eight inches in diameter which could be heard at a considerable distance along the levels. The lead-covered cable ran down the pumping-engine shaft and carried, via the nearby Skip Shaft, away to the levels from 80 to the 278. The "enunciator" was apparently in the whim-house, which bore the proud title of "Levant Telephone Exchange". This was a marvel of communication for the men down below, who could talk to other parts of the mine or to the captains in the count-house. The telephones at Levant were a complete success, and the writer is proud to record that their installation was carried out by his grandfather, Valentine Corin, A.M.I.E.E., of the Anchor Foundry, Penzance. In those days a foundry could supply all sorts of equipment, including a kitchen range, a bicycle, a lavatory cistern or gear wheels, all made on the premises. The Anchor Foundry also marketed Hunningscone-Deckert domestic telephones.

Although the Levant company seemed reluctant to replace worn-out and antiquated machinery like the 1840 whim engine and the 1857 man-engine, it nevertheless covered the site around its shafts with buildings and plant, as shown in the sketch map. Unfortunately the majority of photographers who visited the mine while it was working chose scenes making the best composition. Thus the area which includes the whim-engine house and the pumping-engine house is well recorded, but others have been neglected and pictures of them are rare. However, Russell Bayles went round the surface workings with a camera in 1930, shortly before the mine closed, and a selection of his photographs appears in this book. They show the extent of the dressing machinery and associated buildings, together with a view of the compressor house and the back of the dry. Apart from the pumping-engine and whim-engine houses all the buildings he photographed have vanished as if they had never been.

In spite of its many buildings and its measure of mechanisation Levant at the turn of the century still employed some six hundred men, in addition to women and boys. At the present day it is judged that when a labour force reaches about eight hundred it is difficult to keep good communications between management and men. How much more difficult it must have been to keep in touch with men scattered in small groups through extensive workings at a number of levels going out under the sea. It has been noted that in recent times, when damaging national strikes have occurred, the West Country workers have been less militant, for various historical reasons. However that may be, the Levant labour force became somewhat militant at an early date. In the 1870s, for instance, there was a strike over pay, and in 1882 another over the quality of the candles supplied to the miners. Apparently some were so bad that men had to ride upwards on the man engine without their dim light. Dr Quick was so outspoken about this matter that the press, which reported his remarks, was subsequently excluded from the periodical meetings for a short time. But in general terms Levant was really very liberal in its public relations, better, indeed, than many mining companies today. Certainly the reporters obtained good copy from the antics of the two doctors and of Henry Olds, a St Just butcher.

In 1891 there was a strike over the serious matter of the quality of dynamite supplied. The miners preferred the German product to the British one which the mine supplied. It was admitted that supplies of the latter, which had been on the mine for twelve months, had deteriorated. In the same year there was a strike over the imposition of a time-keeping record. The men's spirit of independence rebelled against the idea of having their names taken as they went under ground. After a short time the management explained that it was only in the interests of safety and in cases of accident, and the recorder, a man known as "Dick Marker", otherwise Richard Grenfell, became an accepted institution.

In November 1909 an institution passed away. Major Dick White died at the age of 78, having remained vigorous to within two days of his death, and having attended a County Council meeting only a few days before that. He was born in Tregeseal, St Just, in 1831, but moved to Trewellard at the age of five and lived there for the rest of his life, looked after by his niece Miss White, for he was a bachelor. He had begun his service with Levant in 1850 as a clerk with the old company, and on its reorganisation in 1870 he acted first as secretary to the provisional committee arranging the formation of the new company and then as purser to the new company, steering it through good times and bad. The Mining World noted that he had been responsible for the equipment, which had enabled the mine to tide over the periods of depression. He always looked on the bright side, and his honourable and upright career commanded the support of all the adventurers. He was described after his death as the Uncrowned King of St Just; and it can be truthfully said of him that he was Levant.

Major White contrived to be purser of several small mines at various times, all situated within an easy distance of Pendeen. He also became Chairman of the St Just Rural District Council, a County

The only known photo showing part of the man engine house. The men posing are almost certainly visitors.

Penlee House Museum.

Man Engine

Sketch of Man Engine and surface machinery.

Bill Newby

To Dry

12ft

Councillor, and a JP, which cannot have left him much time to command his company of Volunteers. His career was somewhat marred in 1893 by the great quarrel with Captain Henry Trezise, who had joined the company in 1862 as an agent and who had been mine manager in 1875-82 and 1891-93. He had made considerable contributions to the revival of the mine, and after a row in the committee of management he was dismissed. So White remained supreme, a patriarchal and much-respected figure, recorded in the verses mentioned above:

> The First is dear old Major
> Who is beloved by all; He's Manager and Purser
> And rules both great and small.

He must have been a comparatively wealthy man, for he eventually owned one-eighth of the mine. He always appeared on the mine immaculate in top hat and frock coat, and photographs of him show that he was something of a "swell", with a silver snuff-box on a chain, and, no doubt, a gold watch-chain as well.

On his retirement in 1907 from active service on the mine he was presented with a silver-mounted liqueur set with a card case underneath, a fitting reminder of his care in making the celebrated count-house punch. At his funeral, and funerals remain a notable event in the life of west Cornwall, hundreds of people assembled outside his residence and the blinds were drawn in all the houses and business premises on the way to Pendeen church.

The Cornishman newspaper listed all the numerous notable people who attended the service, and a number of other mines in the county sent their representatives.

Major White was known throughout the Cornish mining industry and in mining camps abroad, and his passing was seen as marking the end of an era. His hospitality and unbounded geniality made him welcome wherever he went, particularly among his friends at the Western Hotel in Penzance. On one celebrated evening he was told that his carriage was at the door. On going there he exclaimed that it was not his. To this his friends responded "Get in. Major, it's all right". He found that they had presented him with a brand new carriage as a token of their esteem and affection.

At an earlier period the Western was run by the parents of George Henwood, the writer of essays on Cornish mining. For long after the death of Major White the Men Only Bar in the hotel remained the venue for the "characters" of Penzance and district, right until fairly recent times. Alas they have followed the Major to join 'the great majority' and the Western has been demolished to be succeeded by a Social Security building, in sympathy with the times. At least it does not disfigure the town, unlike a previous related Government building.

A year after the Major's death there was labour trouble of a different kind. It was not militant strife but the effect of men voting with their feet against the low wage rates of the mine. They were emigrating in numbers to foreign mining fields and taking their mining skills with them. It reached the stage when the importation of foreign miners was suggested, though this did not come to pass at Levant, only at Geevor after the Second World War, when Poles and Italians joined the labour force.

At one of Geevor's latter day Annual General Meetings one could see a man, apparently a dark stuggy Cornishman, go up for a long service award, and find out that he was an Italian. Those who knew the characteristics of Poles and Italians may ponder the products of intermarriage with the Cornish, a formidable combination which has only served to enrich Cornwall.

The First World War brought another shortage of labour, with miners called up into the army and put on mining work of a highly destructive nature on the Western Front, that of laying huge explosive charges under the enemy lines. In 1917 real trouble flared. The men had joined the Dockers' Union, later to become the Transport & General Workers' Union. That the management at Levant reacted strongly to such a novel situation is not surprising. The union demanded higher wages and was prepared to accept arbitration by the Board of Trade. The Levant manager was instructed to meet the Union, make no concessions, and indicate that the mine's committee of management would not be dictated to, a situation all too familiar in more recent years in British industry. But it must be remarked that back in 1906 Levant had actually introduced something like a modern profit-sharing scheme. The men as a whole body were to be given a sum equivalent to one-tenth of each dividend paid, as a bonus. Unfortunately the idea did not last beyond two payments, and was considered a failure.

In February 1918 the mine refused the union's demands for an increase in wages and a minimum wage rate. At the same time the shortage of labour persisted, a situation which normally leads to an increase in wages. In July a management offer of a 10% increase in wages, but no minimum wage rate, was rejected by the union. A serious strike followed, accompanied by extreme militancy, so that the Chief Constable was asked for police protection at the mine. Violence was being threatened and intimidation carried out; protection was offered to men who wished to work and bonuses for those who would keep the pumps going.

Womenfolk assembled near the Count House on day 2 of the Man Engine Disaster in October 1919.

Courtesy Royal Institution of Cornwall.

In the same year Captain Francis (Frank) Oats died and another great figure passed from the Cornish mining scene. Besides his quarter share in Levant he had also been a major shareholder and joint chairman of the Basset Mines in Chacewater, whose buildings remain virtually intact but roofless. The Oats family retained Frank's interest in Levant, and his son Colonel Francis Freathy Oats, who had served in the Royal Garrison Artillery, took matters in hand and threatened to close the mine. The threat brought a settlement of the dispute, but for the management it was something of a Pyrrhic victory. The final terms, though, were in a sense enlightened. They were 20% on earnings of £6 a month and under, 15% on £6 to £8 per month, and 10% on over £8. Even allowing for inflation a low wage level is revealed, remembering that these wages were per month. But it must be remarked that the variation of the percentage awards over the various wage brackets was much fairer than an across-the-board method of most present-day wage settlements, which benefit the highest earners most and the lowest earners least.

However, the summer of 1919 brought a re-run of the dispute. There was another rejected wage demand followed by a threat to close the mine. In July, in view of an impending coal strike, all surface machinery was stopped except the man-engine, whim-engine and pumping-engine. The previous strike had also led to the flooding of the lower levels, and the mine was obviously just staggering along. On October 20th of the same year the man-engine suffered a disastrous accident. Thirty-one men were killed, the second worst disaster in mining in Cornwall, eclipsed only by the 36 men who died in 1846 in the flooding of East Wheal Rose in Newlyn East by a sudden deluge. After the accident Levant entered into a period of terminal decline.

The death of 31 men and injury of many others affected the district deeply, and over seventy years later the memory lingers on. Surprisingly a considerable number of visitors coming to the whim-engine house have heard of the disaster and are interested to see a section of the man-engine rod and have its functioning explained. It was all too typical of Levant that it should still be operating a man-engine. The ride to the bottom of the shaft took half an hour, followed by a walk out under the sea, which could be a further mile. Such a loss of time added to the cost of distant undersea operations, already inflated by ore-handling costs, led to the consideration of straightening the Skip Shaft so that men could ride in it, but like other good ideas it came to nothing. Whether it could have served for hauling ore and men and sending down tools and timber is doubtful.

The man-engine had been the scene of casualties during its period of use, and four men had been killed at various times and a number of others injured. Boys were accompanied for their first three or four trips underground, after which they were on their own, by the light of a tallow candle. It would hardly have pleased the present-day Health and Safety Executive, but the management did not forbid visitors to the mine to ride the man-engine. One, writing of a visit in 1887, quite cheerfully rode it, remarking that it claimed a man occasionally. It very nearly claimed him through a little error in placing his foot. On returning to surface he met two ladies who had been offered a trip underground, but who wisely declined when they learned what would be involved.

Apart from the occasional casualty the management was none too careful about the man-engine. When it was extended in 1888 no knocker or signalling line was provided, and the Inspector of Mines saw to it that two members of the committee, who were large shareholders, were sued. Events cast their shadow before them, for twenty years later there was a serious accident. Between fifty and a hundred miners of the forenoon shift were ascending to the surface when a length of the rod broke. Several men were thrown down the shaft. Others were severely shaken by the sudden drop. Stones and debris fell down the shaft, and it was with considerable difficulty that severely injured men were brought to the surface. The wildest rumours circulated concerning the extent of the accident, but the management seems to have been little roused by the incident. If there had been an energetic Inspector of Mines like Clement Le Neve Foster (distinguished in his time for his great concern for miners' health and safety, who was later knighted) who had taken action over the lack of a knocker line, there might have been more response.

The man-engine was not without safety devices. The rod had wings, or catch-pieces, with corresponding sills, stout pitch pine beams, in the shaft, so that when the rod was at the bottom of its stroke there was a small uniform space between wings and sills.

Presumably in 1908 the wings and sills had prevented the detached portion of the rod from falling very far, but even then there were several casualties. On the afternoon of October 20th, 1919, the safety devices failed in their function. A full shift of men was ascending, which could have increased the load on the machine to up to 24 tons.

Experienced men noticed a strange vibration in the machine and those fortunate enough to arrive at surface very soon noticed that they had not been followed. Someone went to look along the connecting tunnel to the shaft and found that the engine had gone. The rod had parted from the beam. One man was seen standing on the first sollar and quickly rescued, but too bemused to give any information. But it was all too apparent that the rod had parted from the beam at the surface. It had happened at the top of the upward stroke. There were no sollars or ladders left. The rescue parties had to make their way down the cliff to enter the mine by the adit.

In falling the rod got out of line, destroying the sills and catches, and broke in two at 60 fathoms below the cap, so that the upper part, with thirty men on it, fell 46 fathoms to the 70 fathom level, destroying platforms as it went. This caused most of the casualties. The scenes of carnage were something which those involved remembered until their dying day.

Geevor Mine sent men to aid the rescuers. Two men could not be released for twelve hours. With a third man it took 48 hours to bring him out, but he died shortly after. The last body was brought out five days after the accident, a testimony to the enormous difficulties encountered by the rescue teams.

Back in 1970 under the heading Yesterday's Witness BBC2 transmitted a programme on the disaster, when eyewitnesses could still be found. Even in cold print it takes little imagination to envisage the horrors so graphically described, especially if one has ever been underground. In 45 minutes, mainly through the interviews with witnesses, the programme touched on most aspects of the case. Even looking back half a century the speakers had the eloquence of their generation. One is tempted to include the whole transcript as an appendix but quotes from some of the more dramatic passages must suffice. One of the first rescuers was William Angwin, who went down the ladder road:-

"The ladders was swingin' forth and back, I found it very dangerous. A moan came from a man in front of me and there was a little piece of ladder there. I made to grip the ladder to save myself 'cause it shook me. I was bunch of nerves, believe me, and there he was with all the slush and everything running from the shaft, right down his face and mouth, and he was pinned by his right hand and knee to the wall of the shaft one side, and the left hand outstretched and jammed that side. He started to moan and groan again so, what I done, was put some timber there to ... took away the water that was runnin' in his face, and he was feeling very ... like he wasn't ... closed up then, went quiet so I guessed that I'd done something for him. Poor fellow he was picked up 'bout 5 o'clock in the mornin' ... He died later".

Albert Dymond said: "And I had a mate, he was there for a day and a half to two days and when he came out — seen 'un day or two afterwards, 'Well, what it was like, boy?' 'Well,' he said, 'it was like 'ell — a mass of fire with the iron and the wood and the stones all comin' down', he said, 'a mass of fire'. An' he was there for a day, day and a half standin' on this 2ft platform or step holdin' on to that. No light. He could'n move 'cause he didn't know whether he'd go down farther or not. He was there 'til someone fetched him out.'

The newspapers carried stories of rescue and escape. Willie Lawrie, a bright young lad, had started underground only about three weeks before and had a very narrow escape. He said: "I was two steps above it what we call the 80, that's 80 fathom. I was two steps above that when the engine broke away and I was dug out two steps below that — a matter of 48ft. Now the man that I worked with, he was a step above me and he was found down 110, and the man that was below me, a man called Willie Watters, he was dug out before they found me, and he was dead. So actually I was very, very fortunate. I had 36 stitches in my face and neck, lost all my front teeth, a collar broke, and eight ribs crushed. But — took me 12 months before I started to work again."

John James said: "We was stretcher bearers, you know, has to take 'em back, found two down where I was doing in 50 level, one down and one up the next stage. We brought they two back, in there 'bout

The whim engine at an early stage of restoration. In the foreground the sweeprod, crank and flywheel. Above the last is the top break-block. In the background the valve-gear, valves and cylinder.

Bill Newby.

hour and half we was, then we got sent from there up 60 level, went up there and brought three or four back, dead. The we's sent from there up 24 level and I think I, without tellin' a lie, I think we carried twelve back from there that night. I was afternoon shift. I went down 2 o'clock and never went home no more till 8 o'clock next evenin' and 'bout 12 we carried out there and two of them was our neighbours here. Yes, funerals here, funerals there, for days and days and days."

For those unfamiliar with Cornish parlance it should be noted that Albert Dymond, above, addressed his mate as 'boy'. This form of address bears no relation to the age of the person addressed! In fact it used to be said 'There are no men in Cornwall, only boys!' A young son would be known as *e.g.* Boy Harry. 'Boy' is now out of favour with a younger generation.

Bad news travels fast, so it is usually said. But on this occasion it was slow to reach St Just, only two miles away. There would have been few telephones in the area. Indeed, it may be thought remarkable that Levant, slow to embrace change, had one, until it is remembered that the mine had underground telephones in 1895. It was only when Levant's private mail bag failed to arrive at St Just Post Office that a phone call was made to the mine (connected to the public system at Penzance in 1912) by the Postmaster, Joe Williams. He spoke to George Polgreen, the Secretary of Levant, and later the Vicar of St Blazey for 33 years, having taken Holy Orders. To the enquiry of what the trouble was, Polgreen replied, "Don't ask me Joe. God knows what's happened over here yet." Perhaps the task of visiting those bereaved by the disaster caused George Polgreen to turn to God.

An official inquiry was held by an Inspector of Mines. The whole subject was very thoroughly examined in great detail. The conclusion of the cause of the failure of the engine was very simple. The rod was attached to the beam at the top by two strap plates, in the shape of an elongated U. It had been annealed three years before, but a close inspection when it was hot had failed to reveal a flaw in its manufacture which led to the eventual breakage. A melancholy reminder can be seen in the broken strap at Geevor Museum.

The Inquest Jury's verdict was "accidental death". Such a disaster would no doubt bring more legal consequences today. A fund was set up for the dependants of the dead men. The last living link with the disaster was Mrs. Anita Murley, "Granny Murley" as she was affectionately known in the district. She died in September 1985 at the age of 93. When her husband was killed she had two children and a third was born on the Boxing Day after. She lived on a small pension from the Disaster Fund and earlier in her life took in washing to supplement it. Three years before Mrs. Murley's death subscriptions were raised from private individuals and a memorial tablet listing the names of those killed in the disaster was placed in Trewellard Chapel at the top of Levant Road. It was duly unveiled by The Viscount Falmouth, Lord Lieutenant of the County.

FINIS?

"We got on top of this cliff and I thought, where in the world are we going? We had to go down over the cliff, walk down over the old pathway, zigzag all the way down and we got right down. The sea was down there and we had to walk across planks to get into the adit in the bottom of the cliff to get to the shaft."

Leslie Rawlings, being taken down Levant on his first day in 1925.

CHAPTER SEVEN

An almost immediate result of the disaster was that at long last the only surviving cost-book company admitted it needed new capital. It had no reserves under its antiquated system of book-keeping and the result was that, just before Christmas 1919, shareholders were informed that agreement had been reached with Geevor. A new limited company was to be formed to take over the working of Levant, with an authorised capital of £160,000 in 10s shares, of which 40,000 would be allotted to the existing shareholders in Levant in exchange for their shares, 200,000 would be allotted to Geevor for cash, and 80,000 would be held in reserve. The new company, Levant Tin Mines Ltd., was registered in February 1920 in 320,000 10s shares. The board of the company was headed by Oliver Wethered, chairman of Geevor, assisted by Colonel F. F. Oats, Lieutenant-Colonel Giles Oats, and J. Vivian Thomas, a solicitor. In 1925 St John Winne, a director of Geevor, and Professor James Gunson Lawn, C.B.E., joined the board. Lawn was an eminent mining man who, among other things, had written the standard work on mine accounting as early as 1897; and Col. F. F. Oats had received a mining engineer's training at Freiberg in Germany.

In May 1920 90,000 shares were offered pro rata at par to Geevor shareholders, and by agreement 62,500 shares, credited as fully paid were allotted to Geevor, the total representing 52% of the company's capital. Until February 1922 a further 80,000 shares were under option in case the company needed further capital, but the option was never exercised. Shareholders in the liquidated company, besides receiving shares in the limited one, received 16s 9d cash per share, of which 9d per share was deducted and paid to the West Cornwall Infirmary. The adventurers must have felt that they owed the hospital something, for in 1883 they resolved to contribute two guineas a year to it.

In the meantime there was the pressing problem of working the mine without the man-engine. Operations were suspended after the accident and were not resumed until the formation of the limited company. The captains suggested clearing the Man-Engine Shaft and putting in a gig, with a new winding engine. If only the Skip Shaft had been straightened as suggested in 1895, at least a temporary solution for winding men could have been achieved. A third of the men's time was lost in going to and coming from the submarine section, implying a loss of £6,000 a year. But when the cost was estimated at £30,000 the adventurers rejected the idea. It is said that Frank Oats then offered to sink the shaft at his own expense, if he could have all the ore met with on the way. It would have been a fair gamble, as the shaft would not by definition, have followed the lode down. Oats then caused some lavish expenditure on the mine, which gave a false feeling of prosperity and gave pay to men who might

This panorama of Levant in the early 20th century shows the condenser water settling tank serving the whim engine.

Captain R. S. Alston

William James Rowe, the last engine man of Levant's whim engine.

Trevithick Society Collection

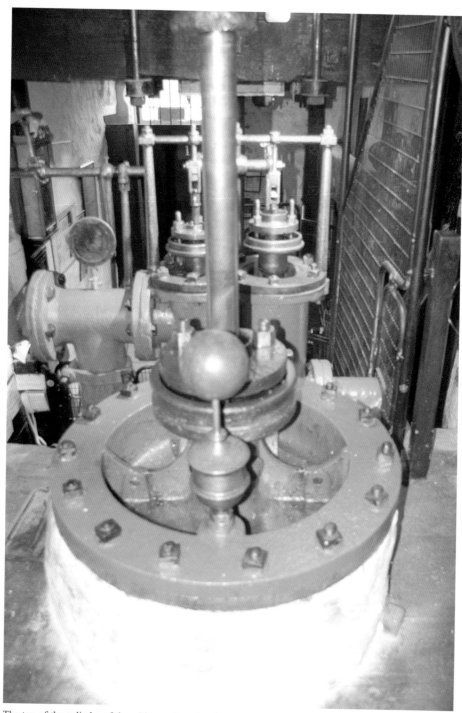

The top of the cylinder of the whim engine, showing the piston rod attached to Watt's parallel motion. The motion, so to speak, translates the straight up and down of the piston to the arc, which the indoor end of the beam is describing. In the foreground is a pre-mineral oil lubricator. The chamber is packed with tallow, the weight of the ball forces it down and the heat of the cylinder melts it.

Chris Quick

otherwise have gone to the Madron workhouse. That institution maintained a dismal way of life for the destitute, until the arrival of the Welfare State.

It was finally decided to sink a new vertical shaft. The site for it was chosen some distance east of the compressor house. Here a patch of level ground can be seen, covered with heather, where the ground had been cleared to sink the shaft. But no further work took place, and the heather spread over the ground, where the soil composition had been changed. A winding-engine bought from the Basset Mines, Chacewater, was never erected or put to use.

In the absence of a new shaft there was little choice of a way into the mine. There was no point in using the ladder road of the pumping-engine shaft, and the alternative was to go down the cliff into the narrow cleft of Levant Zawn and to enter the mine by the adit. The visitor peering into the zawn from a point near the whim-engine house may consider the choice as one of two evils. The new company inherited a vast amount of antiquated and worn-out equipment, and Thomas Robins Bolitho blamed the mineral lords for this. There had certainly been years of negotiations for a new lease, and until it was secured the company had been reluctant to incur capital expenditure. The mine had the misfortune to have three sets of mineral lords. One was concerned with mineral rights below the land (originally Messrs. Robyns, Trezise and partners) while the Duchy of Cornwall held the rights to the part between high and low water. Below low water the third party was the Crown, in the shape of the Office of Woods and Forests. The last-named described themselves as "lords of the undersea leases of South Trewellard Mine", but nowadays it is the Crown Estates Commissioners with whom companies like Levant must deal. The adventurers in both cost-book companies had cause for grievance in that one of the lords had formulated unreasonable terms for his lease, and was not prepared to discuss them. There was also the lords' insistence on the payment of royalties on mineral sales even when the mine was running at a loss.

In the end new leases were concluded when the limited company took over, but because of the deficiencies already noticed the company was obliged to abandon the submarine part of the mine, since men could not be expected to climb down to 350 fathoms or 2,100 feet, which would have rendered their labours uneconomic. The men did, however, climb down and up from the 190 fathom level below adit, or 1,140 feet. However, when they reached the mouth of the adit, with the climb up the cliff in all conditions of wind, rain and sea spray, they did not have a covered way to the dry. But despite the discomfort they were just glad to have a job.

Despite the abandonment of the submarine section, the working of the less-rich landward lodes, and the fall in the price of tin after the First World War, production of tin was quite good. Freathy Oats carried out development between the 130 and 190 fathom levels. It was remarked by another Bolitho, Horton, that Freathy Oats "lived for ten years on ground that had been abandoned in my grandfather's time". The mine staggered on against all the odds and its manifest deficiencies. As it was more recently said about a great surviving mine in Cornwall, it seemed to be a mine they could not kill, for all its century and more of ups and downs. But the end came in October 1930, in the depths of a world economic depression. The price of tin was dropping and had fallen to £99 per ton. A notice appeared in the dry stating that the mine would close the following Saturday. Of wages due a third would be paid following the sale of machinery and timber, a further third at the next Christmas and a final third the following Christmas.

Some years before this the Treasury had granted a £10,000 loan through the Trade Facilities Act Committee. As soon as the Company collapsed the Treasury appointed a liquidator and in the event all the plant on the mine, save the whim engine, was sold for scrap at the ridiculous sum of £600 and over 200 men had been thrown out of work. It took the heart out of the St Just mining district, where only Geevor remained to somehow survive. An institution had passed away.

The late Jack Trounson (President of the Trevithick Society 1981 to 1987) was then a young mining engineer, and engaged the interest of Josiah Paull, a director of South Crofty. Captain W. H. Ellis, the mine's former underground agent, compiled a report. Perhaps the most interesting part of the report is that he favoured an inclined shaft. (Such a shaft ultimately came to pass, but of that more later.) The incline would follow the richer values in the killas further westward, following the main ore shoot, save a great amount in tramming and provide better ventilation in a hot mine. Such was the temperature that it was said that it took three men to do two men's work. There would be a great saving in time in getting men to work and it was envisaged that the shaft would go down to a 400 fathom level. Captain Ellis reckoned it would more than offset the extra cost of sinking, extra hoisting power and higher maintenance costs.

Josiah Paull opined that the mine would make an excellent prospect in better times, but Jack Trounson's efforts to find backers were in the worst of times and, lacking contact with the City's capital markets, were unfortunately unsuccessful. Nevertheless, a few years later Jack was one of a small team of enthusiasts who saved the whim-engine from destruction and laid the foundations of the Trevithick Society.

However the time had not quite come to write FINIS to the Levant story.

GEEVOR INTO LEVANT

Lovatt said to me one day — the weather was pretty rough — I wasn't more than 14½, "Do you think you could go down and shut that water off (in the 40) Leslie, my son." I went in and I heard something roaring in there, I can hear un now. It scared me, I tell you straight. My hair stood on end. I thought, well, I'm going back? I'm going to tell Lovatt there's something in there. But I thought then I mustn't, they'll pull your leg then long as a wet week, the old miners would, and I kept going. I went back and went up and I didn't say nothing to Lovatt. But the job was done and I was afraid Lovatt was going to say to me "Go down and turn the water on, boy." Anyhow he said, "Come on, boy, we'll go down and see to the water". Then I come there and I said "What's that up there, Lovatt, sea upthere?" He said "Tha's nothing my son, tha's nothing, tha's nothing!"

Leslie Rawlings in Levant 1925. Recorded in 1991.

CHAPTER EIGHT

Levant had been closed, or "knacked" (knocked) as they say in Cornwall. Even so, it was not uncommon for an abandoned mine to be reopened by an optimistic company. But Levant inherited a dire legacy from the former management — the so-called Forty Backs. This term was a byword for a weak spot in the roof of the 40 fathom level. The trouble went right back to the days of Captain Henry Boyns, who, when he retired as manager in 1875, took the mine's section of the Forty Backs home with him, and it was not reunited with the other sections of the mine (then at Geevor) until some ninety years later. In the level the miners could hear boulders rolling backward and forward on the sea bed when a heavy sea was running. Boulders is not an exaggeration: the sea is capable of moving rocks the size of a room in an ordinary house. In 1866, when Captain James Evans, of North Pool Mine, Chacewater, was manager, Warrington W. Smyth reported to the Duchy of Cornwall Office that sea water was coming in the Forty Backs. Further excavation was stopped and additional timber supports were put in. This action seems to have taken place following two refusals of the men to go into the mine, such was their concern.

In 1869 the old company was in disagreement with the lords over the Forty Backs. Captain Joseph Vivian of Reskadinnick, an eminent mining engineer at the top of his profession, carried out a further inspection, with which Smyth agreed. The lords were concerned with the safety of the mine and their revenue, though The Cornishman newspaper remarked that "the safety of the men was apparently a minor consideration, not even worth mentioning." Perhaps the lords thought the safety of the men was implied.

There is often a lighter side to potential disasters, and this one was no exception. One pare of men in the 40 fathom level kept complaining to the captain of sea water which seeped in, but he would not accept that there was any. One of the pare was from Sennen, on the coast about six miles towards Land's End. On his long walk to the mine he collected some limpets and placed them on the flow of water. So the captain admitted its saline nature! (Perhaps the record walk to work was that of a miner who worked in one of the lower levels of Dolcoath and walked five miles there and five miles back, six days a week for forty years.).

To make the Forty Backs safe the lords' advisers suggested that a strong arch be built, but Smyth objected on technical grounds. Later Captain William ("Kimberley") James, a member of the committee of management in 1883-93 and from 1899 to 1916 manager of Basset Mines, who had started as a working miner in Levant and who had worked in the Backs, recommended something similar in bricks and cement. But Major White thought it would mean that the miners would be afraid to work in the mine while the building was proceeding. In the event the timbering put in lasted the life of the mine, but not long after its closure.

A grave error in surveying had been made in measuring the depth of the sea above the Backs. In the nineteenth century it was put at 6 or 6½ fathoms. In the 1960s it was found to be 45 feet. It would not have been too difficult to indicate the place to take a sounding from the surface of the sea. A boat could have been found from Portheras Cove to the north-east and a series of soundings could have been taken with a simple lead line. Of course they could have found no indication of the state of the ground forming the roof of the Backs, but they had certainly miscalculated its thickness. The point is that the sea eventually broke in and the fact was confirmed when Geevor, having noticed that the water in Skip Shaft rose and fell with the tide, put fluorescene dye down the shaft. A few days later it coloured the sea around the breach.

When the ghost of the wicked Tregeagle was laid it was bound to the task of emptying the reputedly bottomless Dozmary Pool on Bodmin Moor, with the aid of a limpet shell with a hole in the bottom. Dewatering Levant without completely sealing the sea breach would have been reminiscent of Tregeagle's labours. So Geevor, having already decided that its ore reserves were not sufficient without expanding its operations into Levant and developing that mine in depth, resolved as a first step to seal the breach.

The first attempt to seal the breach in the sea bed was made in 1961, when divers placed a concrete plug in the hole and put a reinforced concrete mat over it. But unknown to the engineers there was a wide gunnis with unstable walls and roof below the hole, where the lode had been taken away, and the action of the sea soon broke up the concrete mat. There was then a long pause for thought, for it was clear that the cost of sealing the breach would be high. As many of Levant's miners had put their labour and skills into developing the mineral wealth of South Africa it was fitting that the Union Corporation of South Africa Ltd. agreed to join with Geevor in sealing the breach and to contribute three-fifths of the cost.

So in 1965 a second attempt was made to seal the breach. It began with pumping 30,000 gallons an hour of sea water out of Skip Shaft. This had the effect of drawing loose material from the sea bed into the mine to within a few feet of the bedrock, so that the bottom of the new plug would rest on natural fill. The remains of the old concrete mat were then removed, and a wall of sandbags filled with quick-setting cement was built round the hole for a good distance on either side of the breach. This gave the divers steady water in which to work, and successfully prevented the sea from causing any damage while the sealing was in progress. Conditions at sea were poor for most of the time, and the divers could only work about one day in three. They worked from a 35-foot ex-Admiralty motor vessel, renamed *Wheal Geevor* (Geevor Work), in depths of water varying between 70 and 55 feet. Some 7,000 bags of quick-setting cement were dumped over the side to make a much larger new reinforced concrete mat. Then pipes were installed, leading from cement mixers set up on the top of the cliff and down into the hole. Volunteers from among Geevor's surface workers ensured that a constant supply of quick-setting grouting ran down through the pipes, night and day, for nearly a fortnight. About six hundred tons of concrete were laid under the sea in this way before the breach was filled. As far as is known no comparable feat in terms of distance, depth and location had ever been accomplished before. The technical achievement was remarkable, and won for its projectors the coveted Gold Fields award, the first time it had been awarded outside South Africa.

Life in connection with *Wheal Geevor*, 22 miles from her Newlyn base, was not without incident, although there were no casualties. On July 1st she struck the Vyneck rock off Cape Cornwall through a combination of steering trouble, swell and low water and sprang a serious leak. She was escorted into Newlyn by the Sennen Cove Lifeboat *Susan Ashley*. On October 8th in the same year the weather turned very bad, and those on the cliffs wondered whether she would reach safety, and it took three hours steaming to reach Newlyn.

On one occasion a diver had the feeling that he was being followed and turned to find himself being eyed by *Cetorhinus Maximus*, 18ft in length and weighing several tons. The basking shark is harmless but the fear was that a flick of its tail might sever the air line and the decision was taken to kill it.

Following the success of the sealing, the mine was unwatered, a winding-engine was erected, and Skip Shaft was fitted out with a cage for the transport of men and materials. As each narrow level was unwatered men crept along them — there was just room to crouch — and put out a set of timbers. The sealing was not quite perfect at this stage, and sea-water continued to trickle into the workings. As each set of timbers was put in, the miner, working on his own, would tack an opened-out plastic fertiliser bag to the roof and walls so that he had a dry place to work in. One miner the author met told him he liked this sort of job, because it was a job with a challenge, and that he had gone round the neighbouring farms one Sunday to buy plastic bags at sixpence apiece. Once the timbers were secured the miners shovelled out the debris from under the concrete plug until there was sufficient space to complete the sealing and securing of the roof from within the mine. The work was finished by March 1966, and in 1967 diamond drilling was started in the old workings, including a horizontal hole from the 40 fathom level in the direction of Botallack.

Winch being used underground by a Geevor miner.

Ernie Richards

Now let us detail the development of Geevor Mine, Levant's north-eastern neighbour. After some desultory prospecting in the 1890s the mine was started on a small scale by some miners who had returned from South Africa during the Boer War. In 1906 North Levant and Geevor Ltd. was formed to work it, and in 1911 the company was reconstructed as Geevor Tin Mines Ltd. It was one of the most up-to-date and progressive small Cornish mines, exactly the opposite of Levant. However, Geevor's miners were not much better off than the Levant miners in terms of pay. A Geevor man speaking only recently recalled the inter-war period as a time when they were glad to use furze and cow-dung as fuel and supplement their diet with rabbits.

48

The immediate post war slump obliged Geevor to cease production between February 1921 and January 1922. Again in the years of the Depression the mine closed for nearly all the financial year 1931-1932, so low was the price of tin. But Geevor survived to become an important resource in the Second World War while on the surface of Levant, in the area of the old dressing floors, concrete pillars are a monument to a desperate attempt to produce wolfram for the war effort. In times of peace no Government has sympathy for the problems of the Cornish mining industry. In war it makes frantic attempts to revive production, mines having been left to close in the meantime.

At any rate Geevor after the Second World War became one of the few surviving mines and fairly sound. It was very much part of the Cornish scene as the following rhyme betokens :-

> Down in old Geevor, working all day,
> Boring and blasting for 5/- a day,
> If you don't like it, go where you may,
> Go to the count house and get your back pay.
> Trad.

After the War the International Tin Agreement was established to stabilise the price of tin. The object was not only to prevent the price per ton from dropping too low but also to prevent it going too high. The Buffer Stock Manager would buy when the price was low and sell when it went too high. This scheme worked well for forty years. But once again an event cast its shadow before it. The USA disposed of much of its strategic stock pile of tin. In 1978 Geevor had been riding high. The Annual Report of the Company for that year showed a profit before taxation of over £1 million. Over a 1,000 tonnes of tin concentrates had been produced. This compared with Levant's highest total of black tin 656 tons, in 1904. The slight caveat is that Levant's figure would have been in proper Imperial measure and Geevor's in metric. Nevertheless the great majority of Levant's totals were way below the 600 ton mark. Contrariwise Levant produced a record of 3,620 tons of copper ore in 1896. In this connection it is worth noting that Geevor produced a mixed copper concentrate right to the end. In 1986 it shipped a consignment out of Penzance harbour. That really was the end, the end of a story stretching back into the Bronze Age. At the 1979 Annual General Meeting the Chairman of Geevor was able to announce that the sub-incline shaft from Geevor to Levant had been completed, that Levant would be tapped and drained down to Geevor's 19th level, with a drive from Geevor's 18th, to connect with Levant's 278 fathom main tramming level. (Geevor's level depths are measured in feet, thus the 18th level is at 1800 feet from surface. Levant's measures were below adit level.). It was also revealed that £2 million would be spent on developing and extending the mill. The major capital programme would ensure continuance of working "for many years to come." The Chairman was aware of the critical nature of the price of tin. At that moment the price of tin metal had fallen below £6,500 per tonne, and the Chairman was also aware of the threat of the releases from the U.S.A. stockpile.

At the same Annual General Meeting a presentation of a bowl made from Geevor tin was made to Mr. Bill Roberts to mark his 50 years of service to the mine, which he began at the age of 15 years. There then 342 employees at Geevor, who were paid in total £1.7 million in the year.

Back in the early 1960s Geevor's Annual Report was rather plainer than the plainest Church magazine. In 1974, at the author's suggestion, a plan of the mine showing the lodes in the Geevor sett and in neighbouring mines was included. By 1978 the Annual Report had blossomed into a full colour cover, with a photo of sunset over the headgear of the Victory Shaft, the sun a glowing orb against a red sky.

Seven years later Geevor's troubles began. The 1985 annual Report noted that there had been fears that the Buffer Stock Manager might not hold the market for tin steady. An average price of £9,600 per tonne had been obtained by the mine for the year ending 31st March. On the following 24th October the tin market crashed in catastrophe and dealing in tin was suspended on the London Metal Exchange. It turned out that the buffer stock manager, a Dutchman named de Koning, had run out of cash with which to buy tin and support the market in it. His debts were about £1 billion, with 62,000 tonnes of tin in the buffer stock, and he defaulted on contracts to buy a further 68,000 tonnes. The high price which had hitherto been maintained for tin had not only caused mines to maximise production but had also encouraged consumers to find substitutes, notably aluminium. Anyone who drinks beer from an aluminium can instead of a tinned one can reflect on this. In a figurative sense the sun had indeed set on Geevor and on its hopes of going into good values deep in the Levant sett and sinking another sub-incline shaft from the Victory Shaft into the Botallack sett. In the case of the latter mine work had already been done on restoring Allen's Shaft, on which a new headgear was installed.

The crash naturally affected the other Cornish mines, South Crofty and Wheal Jane, as well as the budding Wheal Concord. A march through London by some 800 Cornish miners and their supporters failed to move the government, who eventually gave South Crofty a loan, but not Geevor. Geevor, not knowing how to repel him, fell under the control of a large overseas shareholder, not a mining man who, thanks to the publicity given to him, was foiled in his apparent intention to strip the mine of its assets and to liquidate the company for his own benefit. His successors continued to operate the profitable tourist side of the mine, developed in later years with trips around the mill and under ground in addition to the museum set up in 1982. But since then it has been a sad tale for Geevor, with the price of tin kept down by over-production by illegal miners from alluvial deposits in Brazil, which took several years to bring under some sort of control. And while there was a rise in the price of tin in 1991 the prospect of any development of Levant through Geevor has now gone, with the closure of the latter mine.

So the career of the old champion Cornish mine has come effectively to an end. Levant was distinguished by its submarine development a mile under the sea, and for many features, perhaps not always for the best. It produced in its life a wealth of copper and tin and even a little gold and silver. If the management over a hundred and ten years had not always been as far-sighted as it might have been at least it was remarkable for its tenacity. The miners, over many generations, worked in very demanding conditions, subject to many hazards, but, like Raymond Harry, were proud to be miners working in the famous Levant. It bred characters as diverse as Dr Quick and Major Dick White. It had its terrible man-engine disaster, which even after seventy-two years is still remembered in the district and seems to have been implanted in the minds of many visitors. Now the hope of a comeback, for the mine was part of Geevor, has gone. And so we may see the last of Cornish mining and tin production after a history reaching down from the Bronze Age.

What of government assistance? In times of peace no government has ever troubled itself about Cornish mining, but in times of war and desperate demand for strategic minerals there are only the abandoned mines to turn to. Like many other accountants, government accountants and ministers only see the bottom line and care not for the death of a tradition, a culture and a way of life; a culture which exported skill in hard rock mining around the world. Some say that the industrial decline of Britain has coincided with the rise of its accountants. A young Pendeen boy said, "I want to grow up to be a miner, not an ice-cream seller!"

The end for the story of Levant? In a sense it is not quite the end. There remains the winding engine, saved from the scrapman in 1935. The story of this engine and its continuance, together with technical details, is told in the next chapter by the Trevithick Society's member, Kenneth Brown.

LEVANT - AND OTHER ENGINES

KENNETH BROWN

How dull it is to pause, to make an end, To rust unburnish'd, not to shine in use! As tho' to breathe were life.

Tennyson

CHAPTER NINE

When the small handful of enthusiasts successfully snatched the Levant whim from the scrap man in 1935, they could not have known that they were starting a new and powerful movement: one that fifty years hence would see large stationary engines preserved and under steam in various parts of the world. Had they been content to rest on their laurels at that point, the engineering world would have been the poorer.

However having saved the engine they were determined to do something about the other 30 or so beam engines still extant in Cornwall, eight of which were still at work. And these included three of the largest pumping engines ever used in Cornwall at the South Crofty and East Pool tin mines in the Camborne-Redruth district.

The first step was to form the Cornish Engines Preservation Committee, bringing in representatives from all the major institutions and engineering firms in Cornwall. Appeals were launched and enough money was raised to form a fighting fund towards the possible purchase of further engines. However it was not long before a second engine was gifted to the Committee, the somewhat larger North Whim on Michell's Shaft at East Pool, which had stood idle since collapse of the engine shaft in 1921. This was the last of the conventional Cornish "fire whims" to be built, in 1887, and the deal included the engine house and the ground around it. (South Whim had also survived but was sadly scrapped during the wartime salvage drive).

However it was becoming obvious that with two engines and houses to maintain, the resources available were inadequate. The decision was made to form the Cornish Engines Preservation Society, bringing in private and corporate members from both outside and inside Cornwall. Lord Falmouth was the first president, Treve Holman, chairman of Holman Brothers chaired the Society while two of the original group, W. Tregoning Hooper and John (Jack) Trounson took over as Secretary and Curator respectively. This took place in 1944, and at the same time the first of the celebrated survey of engines considered worthy of preservation was published. It covered 13 beam engines, pumping and whims, but no example of a stamps engine had survived. There were two other engines in the clay district which for some reason did not feature, including a remarkable double acting, plug handle rotative which lasted into the 1950s.

The Society's first task was to launch a major appeal nationwide. Its aims were described in these words:

The successive contributions of Savery, Newcomen, Smeaton and Watt brought the steam engine into existence. It was introduced in Cornwall to drain the tin and copper mines, but up to 1800 even the best of Watt's engines had a thermal efficiency of less than 2 per cent, or a coal consumption of about 11 lbs per HP per hour.

The Cornish mine owners, situated far from the coal fields were particularly interested in fuel economy. Two of Newcomen's engines consumed 13 tons of coal daily to pump the water out of Wheal Busy copper mine. James Watt's engines reduced this by half; and in little more than a generation from 1800 Cornish engineers had reduced the consumption of the most efficient engines to less than 2 lbs of coal per HP per hour, which equals an efficiency of about 10 per cent. This great advance not only gave an impetus to Cornish mining but had a profound influence on steam engine practice generally. Engineers and scientists came to Cornwall and verified the claims of its engineers by means of independent trials.

It is therefore fitting that these magnificent Cornish engines, which represent the successive contributions of Newcomen, Smeaton, Watt, Hornblower, Trevithick, Woolf, Grose, West, Loam and many other engineers, should be carefully preserved on the sites of their usefulness. They are in truth the last of our Cornish giants.

The proposal to preserve these engines on their sites and eventually to establish a Mining and Engineering Museum nearby, has been warmly supported by the Director of the Science Museum, South Kensington, and by many in Cornwall and elsewhere who are interested in the history of engineering.

The Society estimated that at least £5,000 would be needed to complete the programme in view. But in a statement by the Chairman a year or so later it was conceded that the original plan had been over-ambitious, and proposed that a minimum plan should supersede it comprising:

1) At least one large pumping engine in the Camborne district
2) At least one smaller engine in the clay district
3) A collection of valve gear and other representative engine parts
4) The Society's whim at Levant
5) The care and maintenance of the Society's 30-inch whim at East Pool
6) Trevithick's cottage at Penponds.

It will be seen that today these aims have actually been bettered apart from the loss of the items under (3) whilst under storage.

By 1945 the number of engines in Cornwall had dropped to below 20. The greatest mortality was in the clay district where a number of smaller engines, many having distinctive features, had been replaced by oil engines or electricity. The three engines at New Consols Mine at Luckett, near Callington, went for scrap after standing idle for nearly 70 years, while the South Tincroft 70-inch by Carn Brea station was broken up in 1940. Most surprising of all, though, was the scrapping of Hawke's 85-inch at Killifreth. This went a few months after the Society's formation at a time when the area around the mine was occupied by US troops preparing for D-Day and was thus put out of bounds to the public. What was the writer's chagrin to go there after the troops had departed to find the house empty and grooves in the ground where the bob had been dragged down!

On the plus side, a wealthy American visitor had taken one look at Taylor's 90-inch at East Pool & Agar Mine working and had written a cheque for £500 on the spot to enable the eventual purchase of the engine. It may not be generally known that in 1935 this engine had nearly been a write-off when the top wooden pump rod suddenly "let go" at the start of the steam stroke, causing the beam "to jump 8 or 9 feet into the air". Scars of this accident can still be seen on the engine.

The next mortality occurred in December 1950 when Cook's 90-inch at South Crofty, which the writer had driven, broke her bob and came indoors so hard the engine was a wreck. For some years the Wheal Busy 85-inch had been standing idle as possible insurance should South Crofty have an accident to either of its engines. So it was that one day when Jack Trounson was eating breakfast the phone went, and on came D. D. Belcham, Jack's boss at South Crofty, telling him to go out immediately with a tape measure and see if the Wheal Busy engine would fit the house at Cooks. However he forgot to say why, and Jack was more than a little distressed when he learnt the reason!

Cook's engine sadly went for scrap (or most of it!) and the same fate befell the Wheal Busy engine, the last example from the Perran Foundry, and Robarte's 90 at Wheal Agar which had also been standing for many years. Now with only nine engines to describe, including the Carpalla 40-inch stored in London's Science Museum, the final edition of the CEPS survey appeared in 1953. When reprinted in 1985 there were still 9 engines on the list, a situation which obtains today, a quite remarkable achievement though the future of two clay district engines is not yet finally assured.

In the meantime however there have been dramatic changes in the management structure. Continuing drain on resources keeping the Society's properties weather tight led to their being handed over to the National Trust in 1966. All 200 members of the Society were canvassed for their views and the voting went 128 for, only 2 against. Conditions the Trust agreed to were:

1)   To maintain the properties and engines in good order and repair and in such a way as to preserve their present form and appearance and their present character. In doing so the Trust will have regard to technical advice from time to time from the Society's Council.

2)   Society members will have free right of access to the properties on production of membership cards.

3)   On the properties the Trust will display and sell the Society's literature on a commission basis.

Few will disagree that the ongoing agreement with the Trust is an excellent one.

The final big change came in 1969 when a merger was agreed between the Cornish Engines Preservation Society and the then recently formed Cornish Waterwheels Preservation Society under the new title, the Trevithick Society. It accounts for the fact that the Trevithick Society has recently (in August 2006) donated a 50-foot waterwheel, formerly in Cornwall, to the Laxey and Lonan Heritage Trust on the Isle of Man.* This highlights the fact that the Society is now involved with all aspects of industrial archaeology in Cornwall, and not just engines. But it was the little Levant engine which started it all.

*Formerly known as the Gawns Wheel, from its location on Bodmin Moor, Near Blisland. The wheel is now called the Lady Evelyn.

HIGHLIGHTS FROM THE RESTORATION OF THE LEVANT WHIM ENGINE 1984-1992

MILTON THOMAS ACSM HNC

CHAPTER TEN

My introduction to the whim engine was about 1980, when on a visit to Levant my companion pointed out that inside the old engine house was a Cornish beam engine. We found a fair size stone, placed it near the door, then standing on the stone I managed to grab the lintel above the door and pulled myself up to have a geek through the dirty window. I could just make out the machinery, black and rusty in the gloom. I let go my grasp, half fell off the stone, picked myself up and walked away. At the time I had no idea that about four years later I would be in that engine house at least once a week for eight and a half years supervising its restoration.

The work was done by volunteers who were collectively and affectionately known as the GREASY GANG or LEVANTERS. They came from all walks of life, professional engineers, an accountant, a fine art restorer, farmers, miners, a policeman, a sailing boat enthusiast and his wife, teachers, an engineer from the film industry, a telephonic communications engineer, a motor and mining engineer, an artist, a glider pilot, a stone mason, a local workshop owner with his workshop. Quite a motley crew really and all it needed was to weld them together to do the job.

The reader will appreciate that only a few of the highlights are recorded here as the complete story with the technical details is a book on its own. One would have thought that such a project would have been received with open arms especially from those who profess an avid interest in industrial archaeology, however there was some opposition, not I hasten to add amongst the Greasy Gang.

Be that as it may, it soon became apparent that the job was not going to be straightforward and easy. On some occasions a seemingly small job took three or four visits to complete. So when a problem arose I had to remind the gang that "NOTHING IS EASY AT LEVANT", so stop moaning, groaning, swearing and get on with it. When an individual's spirit did really sag I would whisper "Don't tell the others but you are due for a 100% pay rise next week". However, his pay packet started at zero, so you can work out how much he got.

Initially the objective was to remove the black preservative paint from the engine, paint it white and green, and leave it at that. However one day the London policeman said "Why don't we get this engine working again". Immediately I realised the significance of this remark and so I mused myself

"Cornishmen put this engine here, and here is a Cornishman who will get it working again", at the same time feeling that it would be a fitting memorial to those miners who lost their lives in the man-engine disaster at 2.50 p.m. on Monday, October 20th, 1919. The whim engine was used to bring some of the deceased to surface.

So off came the new paint and now the work really started. All the external ironwork was rusted together in one solid mass of cold metal by the corrosive action of the salt sea atmosphere. The action of the sea air on iron is rapid, I have seen so often that a rusty film will develop in a matter of a couple of days: this will give you some idea of the corrosion after 54 years exposure.

There was no fixed plan for freeing the engine: we decided amongst ourselves who would do what and how. We had the expertise, only a few basic tools were needed such as hammers, files, spanners, pulley and blocks, a propane gas bottle. Eventually the propane gas burner freed all the rusted parts, the secret being to heat them up to a dull red heat. There was a 110 volt lighting circuit, with the power connected to Geevor Mine about 1½ miles away (2km). We were never asked to pay for the power; rightly or wrongly I assumed that the Geevor management was not bothered, or even did not actually know what was going on.

Friday after Friday with the occasional Saturday thrown in for good measure we plodded on in the winter, through the rain and gales, down the cliff path to the engine house door which was always opened before 8.30 a.m. and on many occasions before 8 a.m. This was preceded by a twenty five mile car journey; others came from even further. Summer of course followed which enabled us to gather outside, stretched out on the grass to eat our croust of pasties, sandwiches, heavy cake, saffron cake, crisps and apples, with flasked tea or coffee. Many a problem was discussed and resolved between mouthfuls of grub and cups of tea in the sunshine.

Yes, we were in a good ship with a happy crew, supported by long suffering wives. Our accountant, Will, was over sixty when he became a first year apprentice at Levant. On a fine summer afternoon he was given a file to remove the rust from the air-plug rod, when after about ten minutes he came into the engine house and said to me "I don't seem to be able to clean off the rust with this file". "Why not?" I said. So Will asked me to come outside and have a look, where he demonstrated what he was doing. Unfortunately he was using the safe edge; now I expect a lot of us have done the same thing.

It could well have been the same summer we were removing the debris from the old boiler-house floor using picks, shovels and wheelbarrows. There was one particular large boulder in the centre of the floor that was causing a problem; two or three looked at it, shook their heads and walked away. Another was of the opinion that it might be possible to remove it, whilst a couple more suggested that it was better to forget it and leave it in position. So I called them all together and said "Get that rock out of here NOW". There was a moment of complete silence. Ten minutes later there was only a space to indicate where the boulder had been.

On the same site the next week, a gentleman and his wife were helping us to dig out. The good lady remarked that it was very hot and would we mind if she changed into shorts and loose-fitting blouse. Do you think we objected?

I remember two or more years later we were in the process of diverting some run-off water from the road into a purpose-built tank. I was using a pick to cut out the channel when a new volunteer who had just turned up for the first time said "I think you should dig the channel along this route", indicating the direction by drawing with his foot along the ground. I said "Do you really think so". "Oh yes that is the way", he added. So I promptly gave him the pick and shovel. His route was all right, but there were no more spontaneous forthcoming suggestions.

Let us now return to the engine. An inspection of the steam-pipe flanges and the joints revealed they could not be steam tight. The pipes were dismantled, the skeleton of a bird removed, the flanges made

55

good and new jointing put in. On one particular section, where two pipes of different diameters were joined by a rust joint made in 1840, we had to be very careful not to disturb the joint. We made good the top and bottom flanges of the pipes associated with this joint. All was nicely bolted together with the rust joint intact when Courtney said "Milton, I have a confession to make, I have dropped my knife down the pipe". A silent prayer was offered, the offending knife removed, and the joint is still steam tight.

The photographs of the outside bearing in its before and after state give a clear indication of what can be achieved. The new sleeve fitted onto the drum shaft has been centralised within 1½ thousandths of an inch (0.0037 mm), on an 8½ inch (21.5 mm) diameter. It could be possible that when the sun shines this eccentricity disappears. The sleeve and plumber block were manufactured and assembled by Ron Plaster. The job was completed in about fifteen stages, one of which was to build a pigsty. Our accountant was very perplexed about this, but I said, "Don't worry, when it is completed it will help to bring home the bacon". The pigsty is a mining term given to timbers laid at right angles to each other to act as a roof support, in this case the winding drums. The timbers were brought over from Geevor. One of the major jobs was to remove the piston and reset the piston ring. This was followed by the refurbishment of the air pump and hotwell area, freeing of the valve linkage, extraction and resetting of the Cornish double beat valves and freeing out the handbrake. The photograph shows how the cylinder looked after removing the cylinder cover; the brown streaks are not rust but solidified lubricant. After the beam was levelled the engine was about ready for turning. The pulley and blocks came in handy for this purpose. Every one of these operations was a one off; there was no one to consult as those associated with the engine in its working days were no longer around.

A prime consideration was to keep the engine as a condensing engine in accordance with its original design although one person thought it should be converted to a non-condensing machine. A double acting condensing engine requires a large amount of condensing water, which meant that an outside reservoir must be available. The reservoir or cooling pond was in use when Levant was working, but it had fallen out of use and became a dumping ground for mine rubbish. In addition a large section of the wall on the seaward had lost a lot of its granite stones. This is where the farmers came into their own, and their hedging experience was put to good use in rebuilding the wall; their difficulty was that they could only work from the inside, as on the outside there is a straight drop into the Levant Zawn. So out came the rubbish and about 30 ton of stamps slime was brought onto site. This slime was wheelbarrowed around the top of the now completed wall and dumped and spread around the pond to seal it in conjunction with a plastic membrane. Visitors were amazed to see us wheelbarrowing around the wall, and one German lady and her husband were very intrigued by all of this, so much so she asked me "Is it dangerous out there on ze wall?" with a strong German accent. "No not at all" was my reply "as a matter of fact I will take you part way if you are brave enough". She agreed, so taking her by the hand I said to her "Just keep looking at your husband over there". So out we went, then I said "Now look over your left shoulder". "Mein Gott, mein Gott" she exclaimed "my husband, my husband". "Don't worry" I said "he is over there laughing". A water supply was brought into the pond, from a spring about three hundred yards away, by digging ditches and laying pipes. We constructed a pump chamber, installed a submersible pump, and the job was done.

Once more a brief look at what was going on in the engine house. The cylinder was relagged with a modern non-toxic material. The lubricators on the main journals were made by Reg of Bedford; the brass knobs on the lubricators being taken from his bedroom door, with his wife's consent I hope.

The engine was now ready for a trial run under some sort of power. We decided to use compressed air so a compressor was purchased. We needed to bring the compressor on its low loader to its house near Skip Shaft. Immediately an opinion was expressed by a couple of observers that no way would the low loader negotiate the sharp bends on its final stage to Skip Shaft. What a challenge this raised. At about 10 p.m. on a dark and stormy night the low loader was REVERSED down the slope around the final bend with six inches of clearance between the side of the low loader and a 145 ft. (45m), drop into Levant Zawn. What did we have in the way of lighting you may be wondering. Our illumination

The winding drum before and after restoration.

The 'pigsty' supporting the winding drum.

Cylinder and piston as seen after 58 years of being idle.

Rebuilding the cooling pond, R. Alford and N. Hosking.

General view of the mine from the south. Pendeen Watch lighthouse can be seen in the
distance. *Pete Joseph*

Higher Bal as seen today. This engine house contained a 35-inch engine used for
pumping and winding from Guide Shaft. The shaft itself is behind the wall adjacent to the road.
Compare with the photograph on page 12. *Pete Joseph*

The remains of the compressor house. This originally contained a triple expansion compressor but this was replaced in 1920 by a Belliss & Morecom twin cylinder vertical steam compressor. The stack on the left is that for the calciner while that on the right was part of the stamps engine house.

Pete Joseph

The mine's magazine, to the south and away from the buildings.

Pete Joseph

Part of the copper precipitating section of the dressing floors.   *Pete Joseph*

Not part of an ancient temple but the remains of the Californian stamps battery.   *Pete Joseph*

The dry in modern times. The railings are not original but are in the original location. In the foreground is one of the four baths cast into the concrete floor.

Pete Joseph

The business end of the Holman Brothers-built Cornish boiler in the boiler house.

Pete Joseph

The tunnel leading from the miners' dry to the Man Engine Shaft.   *Chris Quick*

was provided from the Pendeen lighthouse; as the beam swept around the cliff we had for a couple of seconds or so the benefit of its light. The compressed air turned the engine, all our work was well rewarded. George Wall and Willy Alford were particularly involved in turning the engine with compressed air.

The next stage of course was steam. The engine was fully operational from 1.30 p.m. on April 20th, 1993. The 1901 Holman-built Cornish boiler sited in the rebuilt boiler house was generously donated by ECC Quarries Ltd. and was removed and transported from Trethowell Wood, St. Austell in the summer of 1990. This boiler is similar to the type as used by the mine in its working days. It is for exhibition purposes only. A comparison may be made with the modern steam generating unit behind the door at the far end of the building.

The National Trust, the Trevithick Society, a European Architectural Heritage Award, the Midland Bank Plc, the Rural Development Commission, Penwith District Council, the National Trust Penwith Association, and donations to the Steam Appeal funded the project. A number of people provided their services free including the Cornwall Technical College, the Daniel brothers of Liskeard (boiler transportation). Rex Curtis of Roche (boiler lifting equipment), Len Hosking of Sennen (boiler transport), W. Alford (Truthwall workshop) and the Greasy Gang. Just a pointer to anyone contemplating a long term restoration project, you will need ability, patience, determination, flexibility, humour and the knack of getting assistants to do it for FREE. The year 1997 will be the fifth season in steam.

The engine of course needs maintenance which is done at the close of each steaming season. I trust its owners, the National Trust, will keep it operational for at least the next five hundred years as it is a unique part of our Cornish mining heritage. A feature which you the visitor will have noticed is the smooth and quiet motion of the engine. Our Will noticed this as well and said "Do you know Milton the piston rod moving up and down with just the faintest suggestion of a whisper suggests to me the sweetness of a lover's sigh". Time is making its presence felt, some of us are not as well as formerly, and our Will is no longer with us.

However, on behalf of the Greasy Gang. I would like to conclude by saying we are more than satisfied if you have got pleasure from our efforts, and perhaps a quiet thank you as you leave might not fall on deaf ears.

Milton Thomas, captain of the Greasy Gang

65

SKIP SHAFT AND ITS WINDERS
MILTON THOMAS ACSM HNC

CHAPTER ELEVEN

The location of Skip Shaft near the cliff edge was not peculiar to Levant mine. Seven cliff shafts were sited near to the sea, for example Batten's Shaft down at the bottom of Levant Zawn was just above high water mark. In fact the sea occasionally found its way down the shaft. Skip Shaft was sunk on the outcrop of the ore body; consequently it helped to pay for itself as the excavated rock would be sent to the mill for processing. The name Skip Shaft was an obvious choice as it was the hoisting shaft for skips.

A fact overlooked by some writers is that Skip Shaft was also a SERVICE shaft for the mine, and not as sometimes stated that its sole purpose was to raise ore. The underground work force fluctuated between 192 and 509 miners, hence the need for an adequate supply shaft. The miner's requirements would vary according to their occupation. Pares (groups) of miners on rock excavation would require a daily supply of sharpened drills. Stopers, in addition wanted short stull timbers to make working platforms and also to keep the stope open where the hanging wall was weak. Timbermen needed timber for chute construction and roof support. Track layers required new sleepers, rails, dogs (spikes), Jim Crows (rail benders). Sundry supplies would be picks, banjos (short handle shovels), gads (rock chisels), wheelbarrows, sledges, hammers, axes, black powder, dynamite, fuzes, detonators, bal nails (hand made rectangular nails), coal for the underground steam winder, standard ladders, short ladders, rectangular iron box for lowering the ponies, fodder and latrine buckets, iron plates for tram repair, wheels, axles, grease, trial locomotive broken down into convenient pieces for assembly underground. This list is now only indicative. Before the skip, kibbles would have been pressed into service. If the organisation of the mine was good, the supplies would be waiting on the respective shaft stations at the start of the shift. However, as it was the case more often than not, the miners would wait for the skip and then take out their gear. The hoisting of ore started after the supplies were underground. At least two shifts per day would be required. With the advent of the man-engine in 1857, it was stipulated that it was illegal to ride it with tools and equipment; hence the importance of Skip Shaft as a services shaft.

So when did sinking commence? The actual date is unknown, sometime possibly from 1790 or 1800. The collar of the shaft would extend from the surface down to about 10 ft. or so, with I expect some form of wooden structure to keep out the rain to reduce bailing and in addition to prevent the curious from falling in. The two main categories of miners in the early stages would be the sinkers and muckers. Everyone of them was a hardy type. Big men, with muscles of iron and strong backs, and carrying a

Geevor's Skip Shaft winder then......

Bill Newby

......and now

Pete Joseph

granite expression on their faces which came from the environment of their workplace. The sinkers worked on a contract basis in pares of three or four. Threes were known as double handed, that is, two striking the borer, the third turning it: tough on the third if the beater miscued. Fours were known as treble handed, three beaters with one turning. The master sinker charged and blasted the days work. These men were experts in beating the drill, and would quickly set up the beating sequence to an established rhythm, to thump the 1 inch (25mm) diameter drill down to a depth of about 2 to 3 ft. (0.6 to 0.9m), according to the type of ground. Lighting was by candles strategically placed to reflect the light from the polished head of the drill. After blasting it was the turn of the muckers. The muckers would man handle the big lumps of rock into a small kibble (iron bucket), top it up with the small stuff using banjos. A two man operated windlass with a hemp rope would haul it to surface. Windlass hoisting gave way to the use of an animal powered whim with a small headgear. The animals were not necessarily horses; mules and donkeys were sometimes used, though the general name given to such an arrangement was the horse whim. The deepening of the shaft would proceed in conjunction with the lateral development of the mine.

Sometime between the time when the limit of the horse whim was reached and the installation of the 1840 engine it would appear that a steam winder was at work. The development of the mine had reached 180 fathoms in 1836, too deep for horses. Lean mentions two steam winders with 20 inch diameter cylinders in operation. This suggests one could have been at Skip Shaft.

As the 1840s approached the 20 inch engine was on its limit and a revision of the hoisting capacity was necessary. The technology of the day pointed to a larger winder and a new headframe. The headframe would be designed in relation to the winder, its height being controlled by two factors. Firstly at that time the extra height in the event of an overwind did not have to be taken into account, secondly the lower the headgear the smaller the fleet angle of the chain or rope back to the winding drum. Photographs confirm the squatness of the headframe. The 1840 winder had a 24 inch (0.6m) diameter cylinder and a 4 ft. (1.2m) stroke. It was double acting with a reduction gear from engine to drum of 3 to 1, that is three revolutions of the flywheel or driving gear would rotate the winding drum one revolution; this means that a heavy load could be raised at a slow speed. The slow speed of the wind also had the advantage that after the drum had stopped the momentum of the rotating sheave would not be sufficient to keep it rotating against the now stationary chain, thus reducing chain wear. The winding drums were small in diameter, the width between the flanges was narrow in comparison to their height above the drum; they were designed to accommodate a chain, chains being in common use twenty years after their introduction in 1820. The half inch (12.7mm) diameter wrought iron type was in general use with a safe working load of 1.6 ton (1.61 tonne) and breaking load 7.6 ton (7.67 tonne). The chain has the flexibility to wrap itself tightly around a small diameter drum, also it gives warning of a possible rupture when the links show visible evidence of stretching caused by bending stress. It is cheaper and stronger than its predecessor, the hemp rope. The removal of a link would compensate for the stretching of the chain. However it was only as strong as its weakest link.

In 1843 development had reached the 220 fathom (402m) level. Calculations indicate that the hoisting rate from this depth after the wind had settled down would be in the order of 110 ft. per minute (33m per minute), with the engine running at 48 strokes per minute, near its safe maximum, and the flywheel turning at 24 revolutions per minute. The weight of ore in the kibble would be something like 10 to 12 cwt. (0.5 to 0.6 tonne). The ratio of actual load to the safe working load being in the order of 1:3. The problem built into this type of machine is that the number of revolutions at the flywheel has to be sustained as any falling away of the engine speed would reduce the kibble speed in the shaft by a reduction of 3:1, thus adequate boiler capacity was essential.

Once more in order to keep the mine in operation below 220 fathom (402m) a bigger winder was needed. Modernisation at that time would take into account.

— chains to be superseded with an iron rope which was introduced from about 1850.

— a larger cylinder 27½ inch (0.69m) in diameter with a 4 ft. (1.2m) stroke.
— double acting.
— a redesigned reversing mechanism.
— a direct drive to the winding drum.
— a change in the valve operating mechanism.
— probably a bigger flywheel.
— the shaft to be timbered for skip hoisting.

Calculations show the 1840 winding drums were big enough to take a 1 inch (25.4mm) or 1⅛ inch (28.5mm) diameter iron rope to 278 fathom (510m). However, with the small drum diameter the ratio of rope diameter to drum diameter was on the recommended limit with the larger rope, and inside with the smaller rope. Over the limit, undue bending stress would increase rope wear leading to premature failure. The large sheave wheels on the headgear were designed with the same criteria to reduce wear and bending stresses.

So much for the engine, what about the shaft? The shaft would have to be timbered to accommodate two hoisting compartments for 1 ton (1.01 tonne) skips, a ladder way, a small space to operate the signalling system and a new system of skip loading chutes at the hoisting levels. No doubt the alterations to the shaft and engine were done as fast as possible as in the early stages ore hoisting would have stopped. However, in the early 1960s 1 ton (1.01 tonne) skips were coming up at 4½ mph (7.2 km per hour). The Bessemer process of converting iron into steel started in 1856, and the iron rope was progressively replaced by steel ropes. From 1880 development was down to the 278 fathom (510m) level. From this time I suspect that rope replacement was becoming expensive. It is possible that the use of steel ropes and bigger diameter winding drums were on the agenda. In May 1894 N. Holman and Sons manufactured the 5 ft. (1.5m) diameter drums still in situ outside the engine house. It would be good mining practice to equip the new drums with new steel ropes of the langs lay type. The wires forming a strand were wound in the same direction as the strands to form the rope of 1 inch (25.4mm) diameter with a hemp core. The advantage with this type of rope was that it had good wear resistance and greater freedom from weakening through bending. If you require the depths from surface add 25 fathoms (46m) to the above figures: the figures are quoted below adit, about the bottom of the zawn.

At this stage a note on skip loading might not be out of place. The skip filler in the shaft would swing an iron hinged plate across the shaft, so that a skip would rest on it as the skip was being filled from the ore chute. In some cases an iron hood was also put over the mouth of the skip. This hood directed the ore into the skip thus reducing spillage. When the skip was full the filler pulled on the bell line to signal the engine driver to hoist. The skip would then go non-stop to the ore bin at surface. At the same time the empty one in the next compartment would descend for filling. Basically the skip was simply a long narrow rectangular iron box with two sets of wheels on each side to run in guides in the shaft.

Therefore in designing the reversing mechanism on the engine, only the basic positions were required — clockwise, neutral, anticlockwise. The engine driver would operate like this with the loaded skip stationary on the plate in the shaft. The hand brake is on. If the direction of hoisting was to be clockwise the reversing lever would be moved forward from the anticlockwise position into neutral with the left hand, then when in neutral the right hand would slowly depress the tee handle, at the same time the left hand would push the reversing lever forward until a decisive clunk would indicate the clockwise position was set. Release the handbrake, depress with the left foot the pedal to open the condenser water valve, open the steam regulator lever with the right hand, bring the skip to a halt in the ore bin, apply the handbrake. To send the empty one down and bring the filled one up, simply reverse the above procedure to establish the anti-clockwise direction, but not the hands. I have executed this procedure dozens of times with no problems. The change in direction must always be made when the engine is at rest, never in motion. Why? Because with a 1 ton (1 tonne) loaded skip moving in one direction in the shaft, before its direction could be reversed it must come to a stop. At this point the loaded skip

69

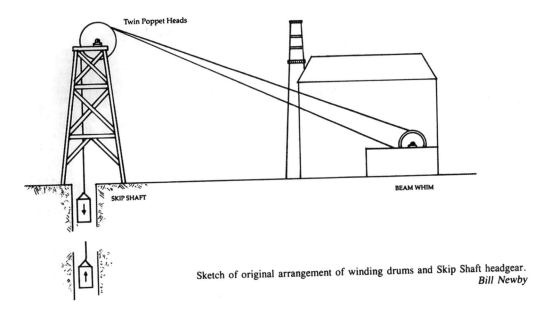

Twin Poppet Heads

SKIP SHAFT

BEAM WHIM

Sketch of original arrangement of winding drums and Skip Shaft headgear.
Bill Newby

The modern Skip Shaft headgear and winding engine house. The small building, extreme right, houses a vintage 3-cylinder Petter diesel, which operates the compressor. This was used in tests of the restored whim engine and acts as a stand-by. The building on its left operated as Geevor's upcast fan.
Bill Newby

could easily run away and take control of the engine with disastrous results. After all you stop your car before you reverse — I hope.

The depth indicator consisted of a circular wooden board about 3½ to 4 ft. (1.0 to 1.2m) diameter on which were fixed two circular metal tracks about 6 inch (150mm) apart. Attached to the tracks were two rectangular metal plates. The upper one had the level numbers on it. The lower one fitted between the tracks to act as a slider, the two were joined by a metal stud. The position of these plates could be altered by undoing the central locking stud and sliding them into their correct position to compensate for the stretching of the rope. It appears there were about 30 plates on the level indicator. There were two pointers, one for the left hand skip and one for the right hand, one turning clockwise, the other anti clockwise. The two diagrams indicate these features. The mechanism which operated the pointers is lost and its operation remains one of the unsolved mysteries of Levant.

Let us now return to Skip Shaft. The installation of the ladder ways for the timbering and maintenance of the skip road were an added bonus in that they were used by the miners to make interchanges between levels. A misconception concerning the man engine is that it took the miners to their workplace. In reality it got them to a station in Man Engine Shaft and from there they still had to walk to either Engine Shaft or Skip Shaft, climb ladders and then proceed to their work place under the sea. At the end of the shift, walk back, climb ladders, proceed to man engine, ride the engine to grass (surface), have a hot bath, walk home — in the rain at times, and so it went on. Skip Shaft was in constant use by miners climbing ladders after the man-engine disaster of 1919. Quite an experience I should imagine, standing on the sollar (platform) or in the ladder hearing and seeing between the gaps in the brattice boards from the light of your candle or carbide lamp, the skip thundering past only 18 inches (0.5m) from your ear.

In 1930 the sound of miner's voices stopped, the smell of black twist tobacco burning in their clay pipes ceased to float up the ladders, the last skip load had gone, the shaft became flooded. The end of Skip Shaft so it would appear. However, like a phoenix rising from the ashes, in the 1960s the shaft was retimbered to take a four man cage, the present headframe erected with its single sheave wheel, and an electric winder was installed in the adjacent building. Depth of wind was 190 fathoms (347m). The object was to rework Levant by Geevor Tin Mines. A lot of money was spent to no avail, because when they got to where the riches were supposed to be the cupboard was bare. The shaft with its levels under the sea are once again filled with water, as is the abandoned Geevor mine interconnected to Levant. It will take a miracle before any mining activity is resumed at Skip Shaft.

All this hoisting required a lot of coal, there is one thing certain, the coal suppliers from South Wales were in constant profit, but not so the mine.

As you look at the headgear, the ruinous buildings, Levant Zawn, the restless sea and the stone steps in the cliff face, it is worth reflecting for a moment of what went on beneath your feet and to 1 mile (1.6km) out to sea from where you are standing, down to the mine's deepest level 350 fathom (640m) below Levant Zawn. A sobering thought is that at least 157 years ago, onlookers saw the beam go up and down, felt the radiant heat from live steam, smelt the fumes from hot oil and grease, the same as visitors do today. Levant as a mine is dead, but not so Skip Shaft winder. I hope the foregoing has added to your visit to that champion of mines Levant.

My thanks are extended to Courtney Rowe for typing of chapters 10 and 11 and for helpful suggestions embodied in them.

Editor's Note. The method of winding described in this chapter represents present thoughts, based on experience in running the engine over the past few years, and is the likely method used. This differs in part from that described in a section of chapter 9 which was based on the best thoughts when that chapter was written about four years ago; it is left there as a record of ideas at that time.

THE LEVANT ENGINE RESTORATION PROJECT
A record of work behind the scenes

BILL NEWBY MBE
Hon. Secretary, The Trevithick Society, 1983-94

CHAPTER TWELVE

At the Council Meeting of the Trevithick Society in August 1984 it was proposed that the 50th anniversary celebrations be centred around the Levant Engine with the object of opening the engine to the public. During a visit to the engine members were appalled by its condition. So, in the November Newsletter, having obtained the permission of the National Trust, the Hon. Secretary invited members to join a working party on Saturday 1st December to begin cleaning and painting the engine. It soon became obvious that the task was greater than anticipated and that an opening date in 1985 was out of the question. Under the direction of Clive Carter the old paint, a mixture of graphite and bitumen, was removed and by the spring of 1986 the engine was painted in a buff colour, like that used on the superstructure of naval auxiliary vessels (some wag suggested that the paint fell off the back of a minesweeper!).

In 1986 the National Trust began the restoration of the building, renewing the roof, re-pointing, providing handrails and a safer access path. By August 1987 the engine was painted in dark green with grey for the valve gear and the site opened to some 500 members of the public on six Sundays during August and September. Collecting boxes invited visitors to make donations, to be divided between the Society and the National Trust, this money covering much of the cost of the paint.

It was then suggested that the best means of preservation would be to put the engine to work. Discussions were held with the National Trust about steaming the engine. If it could be shown that the engine was capable of being moved then consideration would be given to raising sufficient funds to rebuild the boiler house and to provide a boiler. With Milton Thomas in charge of what had become known as the "Greasy Gang" — a term first coined by Giles Clotworthy, the National Trust's Public Relations Officer — the engine was refurbished, with advice from Consultant Engineers, the support of John Treloar, the Engineer commissioned by the National Trust, and a great deal of hard work and ingenuity by the Greasy Gang. Help came from members and local firms, including Geevor Mine who supplied equipment and parts, Cornwall Technical College who refurbished parts in the Engineering Department, English China Clays who donated a Cornish boiler, the Daniel brothers who transported the boiler behind their Burrell traction engine, and many others. The result of many months of work was that the engine moved on compressed air. (The technical aspects of the engine restoration provide enough material for another book.)

The Levant Engine Appeal Committee was formed in 1990, with Lord Falmouth as President, with members from the National Trust, the Trevithick Society and others supporting the project. Designs for a poster by Colin Fearon were approved (a poster which has been used every year since) together with the Appeal Letterhead. Peter Mansfield, Senior Land Agent for the National Trust (later Regional Director) confirmed that National Trust Headquarters had given approval for the project.

Sources of Grant Aid were discussed together with estimates of cost. The Fulton steam plant alone would cost some £14,000 plus a further £5,000 for installation. The target figure was agreed at £75,000 nett, £95,000 overall. The National Trust appointed John Kilroy as fund raiser, and John Dalton as Architect. The Appeal was formally launched in September 1990 in a marquee set up on ground above the engine house, with full coverage from local Press and TV. An application for a European Architecture Heritage Grant was made for submission to Brussels in 1991. The Appeals list was circulated to all National Trust members in Cornwall, to National Trust Associations in UK and overseas, to National Trust supporters, members of the Trevithick Society, and others, in all over 12,000. The National Trust as owners of the site made applications for a Rural Development Grant. But the National Trust could not place a contract for the boiler house until funds had been underwritten. It was suggested that when the Appeal reached three quarters of the target it might be possible to obtain a loan from Central funds, to be met by further responses to the Appeal. Donations totalled £10,000, plus £12,000 from the Rural Development Commission and £5,000 from the Manifold Trust.

By November 1991 when the total cost of the project was put at £128,000, £15,000 had been raised plus the RDC £12,000, the European Architectural Award of 22% of cost, i.e. £27,000, £20,000 from the Midland Bank Affinity Card Scheme and £5,000 from Penwith District Council, 80% of the cost was now available on deposit. There was now no doubt about the ability to go forward, but a determined effort was needed to assure £30 - 40,000 over the next five years. There would be proceeds from visitors to the site and this would depend on the Trevithick Society continuing to provide stewards on a voluntary basis. In November 1991 Peter Mansfield and Bill Newby travelled to Brussels to receive the European Architectural Award by which time building work on the restoration was nearing completion, ahead of schedule, with landscape work and access routes to be completed in the following months.

In July 1992, John Corin's book, "Levant, a Champion Cornish Mine" was launched by the Society's President, Lord Falmouth, proceeds of the sale of the book to be devoted to the Steam Appeal. The book is a best seller and has had several reprints. In August the Fulton boiler raised steam for the first time and adjustments were made. The engine steamed for the first time on 30th March 1993. That same month a totally unexpected but very welcome donation to the Appeal of £10,000 was made by the Mary Webb Trust. This brought the Appeal closer to its target. The balance, currently supported by an interest free loan arranged by the National Trust would be met from entrance fees and be paid off sooner than expected.

At noon on Monday, June 28th 1993 the National Trust organised a gathering of all those involved in the restoration. Lord Falmouth, President of the Appeal Committee, and the Trevithick Society, called the restored engine, "A fitting memorial to the men who worked so long ago at these mines". A plaque to commemorate the event and the efforts of the Greasy Gang was presented to Milton Thomas to be sited on the top floor of the engine house.

Finally, in March 1994, Bruce Millan, European Commissioner for Regional Policy unveiled a plaque which acknowledged the work of the Society, the numerous gifts, and substantial grants. The Trevithick Society continues to provide stewards and guides at Levant, whilst the ever-changing Greasy Gang meets every Friday throughout the year with a rolling programme of maintenance and improvements. The National Trust with grant aid and receipts from visitors undertakes a programme of conservation and improvements to the site.

HIGHLIGHTS OF THE WORK CARRIED OUT AT LEVANT SINCE OPENING TO THE PUBLIC IN 1993

RON FLAXMAN

CHAPTER THIRTEEN

Since opening in June 1993 a lot of additional work has been carried out at Levant. At first, all that was done was to open to the public and steam the engine on six days a week during the summer months. Interested parties could be shown Skip Shaft with the aid of a torch and, when stewards were available, there were guided tours of the site. A small shop evolved in the reception area in the boiler house, this being manned by National Trust volunteers and stewards from the Trevithick Society.

The National Trust owned only the Levant engine and house, but the rest of the site was owned by Geevor Mine. An offer was made in 1992 to buy the Carron Becander electric winder for its scrap value, but the scrap man had already decided to remove it through the roof of the house on the same day that the Trethowel boiler (which had been donated to the Trevithick Society by the then English China Clays Company) was craned onto its footings in the re-built boiler house. To facilitate removal the bed-plate of the winder was cut in half. The air compressor and air receiver were also removed and these were sold, but the winder remained at Geevor covered in plastic sheeting.

The custodian and volunteers knew that there was great potential to expand the Levant experience to visitors. The existence, but not the condition, of the man engine tunnel and shaft was known. Both the shaft and the spiral stairway leading from the miners' dry to the tunnel were filled with rubbish and in the summer of 1996 this was partially cleared. During these diggings a number of iron double hooks were found. These must have been thrown in when the building was demolished and photographs of the dry shows these hooks positioned over the steam pipes above the miners' lockers. Limited access was gained into the tunnel but it was not possible to get right up the shaft because of more rubble, although the tunnel appeared to be in very good condition. The spiral stairway was re-filled to prevent unauthorised entry.

Various other excavations were carried out. Because Levant is on a metered water supply a leat was constructed, starting from a spring near to the old compressor house, and a series of closed pipes and open launders made to feed water to the cooling pond. This water keeps the engine condenser cool and helps maintain a vacuum in the engine for efficient and economical running. What appears to be an inspection pit for traction engines was also uncovered just to the east of the dry. Other excavations revealed a flywheel slot, a curious arched duct near the Count house, and a large coil of decaying winding rope, consisting of wrought iron strands with a hemp core, showing that hemp has a longer life than iron under coastal conditions. A number of improvements and adjustments were carried out during the early years of putting the whim to work, amongst these was the addition of a compound gauge. This enables the driver and visitors to see either the steam pressure or the vacuum within the cylinder.

On the 12th January 1995 the National Trust held a flag raising ceremony at all their properties to celebrate Centenary of the Trust's foundation. At Levant the flag was raised by the Right Reverend Brian Coombes, Grand Bard of the Cornish Gorseth. The occasion was also used to commemorate those who lost their lives in the Man Engine disaster of October 1919. Major White's Punch and Saffron Buns were served to the visitors. There was a further ceremony as a Time Capsule was buried beneath the slate covering the side flues of the boiler. The capsule contained copies of The Cornishman, The Western Morning News, the National Trust's "Cornish Engines" and Trevithick Society publications "Levant, a Champion Cornish Mine", "Cornish Beam Engines and Rotative Winding Engines", the four Levant postcards, the Guides to the Engine and the Walkabout, together with other leaflets and brochures. These events also marked thirty years of co operation between the Society and the Trust.

In 1996 the Trevithick Society was awarded a PRISM grant (fund for the Preservation of Industrial and Scientific Material) from the Science Museum for the purchase and restoration of the Levant head frame, and for the purchase of the electric winder plus the cost of crane hire and transport. The winder was in very poor condition due to having been left in the open during the previous four years. The bed-plate had to be welded together again and an intensive degree of de-rusting carried out. When the winder was craned out originally damage was caused by the slings used for hoisting. The limit switch shaft was bent and its gear wheels had teeth missing, so many weeks were spent rebuilding them and realigning the shaft. It was the ambition of the volunteers to restore the winder and to operate it under its original controls. In order to do this the electrical circuit had to be redesigned because aspects of the original equipment and circuitry were no longer to be used. Although there was three-phase power within the winder house, the power available was limited so it was not possible to use the original 35 horse-power induction motor. A smaller motor was fitted out of sight within the brake pit and an air compressor installed to operate the post brake. Some parts of the winder are still missing to this day, including the tacho-generator and the travelling-light telegraph. The tacho-generator was driven from the main gear box and this fed a voltage to a rope speed indicator and recorder. The telegraph informed the driver if the cage was not moving. This was a well-known phenomenon in the downward direction as the cage was notorious for jamming within the shaft and leaving a coil of slack cable above it! This was because Skip Shaft is crooked and at several points the men riding the cage were used to jumping up and down to free it from the runners as it ran around bends within the shaft. This was a potentially dangerous situation for the riders in the cage. The electric winder was installed by Geevor Mine with a cage that could carry four men and/or materials to the level connecting Levant to Geevor and the new incline shaft.

During 1996 lighting was installed in both Skip and Engine shafts and this always impressed visitors when they looked down. The old ladder-road consisting of 98 ladders in Skip Shaft can also be viewed, although only the top two stages are visible. During 2006 Robin and Charlie Daniels used Swedish pine to refurbish Skip Shaft and its sollars, so there is now safe access to adit level, though not for members of the public. The upcast fan in Engine Shaft, previously used by Geevor for ventilation and radon extraction, was freed up and a small electric motor fitted. It can now be run at a slow speed for demonstration purposes.

October 20th 1999 was the 80th anniversary of the Man Engine disaster. A memorial service was held by the Reverend Kathy Smith and was attended by the Cape Singers and many local people including Elaine George whose grandfather was killed in the accident. The event was recorded for broadcast on local television.

Since the beginning of the Levant restoration great interest has been generated by National Trust publications and coverage by the Press and television. Fred Dibnah came to Levant on three occasions, the first on 23rd June 1998. There is nothing new about Levant Mine appearing in films or television, no doubt helped by its spectacular setting at the top of the cliffs. "Love Story" starring Steward Granger and Margaret Lockwood was partly filmed at Levant in 1944, and the BBC Series "Poldark" starring Robin Ellis and Angharad Rees used Levant in one of its scenes in 1974. The front and end of the electric winder house were covered in hardboard on a flimsy timber framework and painted to resemble a Count House.

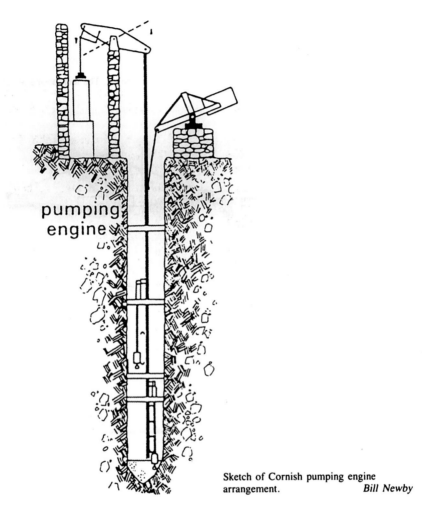

Sketch of Cornish pumping engine
arrangement.   *Bill Newby*

In 1999, having acquired the whole of the Levant site, the National Trust began a programme of consolidation of the various chimneys, shafts and buildings. The arsenic calciner stack had been consolidated some time previously by the County Council. The compressor/power house stack was of particular concern as a large crack was getting wider as each year progressed. The top of the stack was dismantled and re-assembled. Consolidation was also carried out on the stamps engine stack, man engine stack and remains of its engine house, the 1835 pumping engine house, circular powder magazine, electric winder house, temporary winder house (now the video shed), remains of the Count house and compressor house, and consolidation of Boscregan Shaft. At the same time consolidation work was carried out to the engine house and surroundings of Higher Bal. The restoration of the man engine shaft was a major operation.

The shaft head and balance bob pit were restored, the road over the tunnel strengthened, and the clay chute and air shaft reinstated. The top five steps of the spiral stair from the dry to the man engine tunnel

76

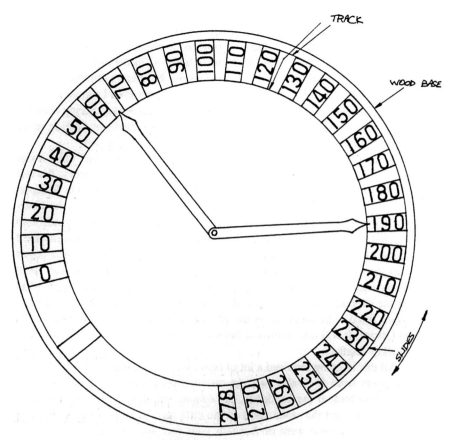

Skip Shaft level indicator - dial

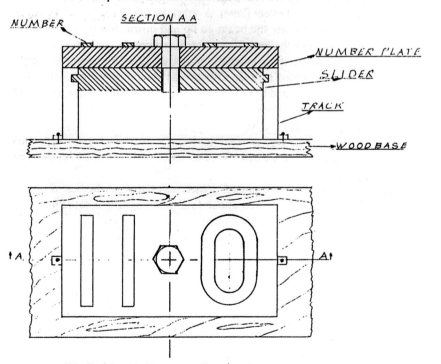

Skip Shaft level indicator - number plate fixing

and the circular coping stones around the top of the stair had been taken away but were subsequently found at a local house and used as a template for new steps which were made at a granite quarry at Mabe. In accordance with original photographs, new handrails were fitted along with new coping stones. An opening ceremony was performed in June 2003 and the tunnel opened for access as far as the head of the shaft, where a mirror is positioned so that visitors can see down the shaft. In 2005 lighting was installed.

In 1999 there were problems with the whim. The cylinder had begun to lean, which caused the piston to run out of alignment. Packing was put under the cylinder but the problem soon reoccurred. The foundations of the granite bedstone under the cylinder were unstable, so during the summer of 2000 the cylinder was raised, a new bedstone cast and the masonry reinforced with concrete and steel girders. There were also problems with the leaking cistern. When the original refurbishments were undertaken by the Greasy Gang, the bottom of the cistern was found to be rotten so concrete was poured in to stop the leaks. The hot well was also out of alignment with the air pump rod trunnion on the bob - it had probably run most of its years of operation like that. A new timber cistern was built, and the hot well and condenser realigned so that a new straight air pump rod could be fitted. The result is a far smoother-running engine. These events are fully recorded in Chapter 14.

The original 110v electrical supply to the engine house was cut off when Geevor ceased mining operations. A small portable generator was supplied to enable the Greasy Gang to work with power tools but in 1992 a three-phase generator was put in the adjacent winder shed to power the new steam plant, oil and water pumps and lighting. This shed had been built to house a small electric winder brought from Malaya and wound from the original head frame. After the generator was removed the shed was used as a store and workshop. It is now the Video Room. John Potter and Dominic Hudson surveyed the underground workings above adit in Levant in 2000. A shortened video of the film which they made, and is now being shown, highlights the extraordinary record attained by Levant in incorporating a number of smaller subterranean mines between 1820 and closure in 1930. This 110 years is the longest period ever of continuous tin and copper mining by one company. A full version of the film (DVD) is on sale in the shop.

Between 2003 and 2005 more works took place including refurbishment of the man engine tunnel entrance, the addition of safety grilles to the shaft, the excavation and partial reconstruction of the tramway tunnel at the bottom of the incline from the stamps, a major reconstruction of the Zawn Brinney retaining wall, the refurbishment of the 1960s drawing office, now used as the custodian's office, and the reinstatement of a large pond as part of the new roadside drainage system.

In 2005 the reception area and shop was moved from the boiler house to the electric winder house and this has proved to be very successful, providing more space for the shop and more comfort for the stewards and visitors. A twelfth scale model of a pumping engine, donated by a Trevithick Society member, is running on compressed air in a corner of the house, together with a model of the man engine constructed by Levant volunteers and working off an electric motor. Also in 2005 the barring motor mechanism for the whim was vastly improved; this is used for pulling the engine away from top-dead or bottom-dead centre.

Since 2005 the landward-side winding drum had been loose on its shaft and this was causing noise when the engine was running. After several unsuccessful attempts, work was carried out during the winter of 2006/7 to replace all the rusted bolts with new galvanised ones in preparation for the removal of the drum should this be found necessary. Copper packing was inserted to enable the drum to be re-tightened onto the shaft, but further works were needed to secure the drum. A working replica of the level indicator has now been constructed.

Construction of a toilet block for staff and visitors, with facilities for the disabled, was completed in 2007, along with other measures to ensure disabled access to the site.

The National Trust and the Trevithick Society is greatly indebted to the many active volunteers for their hard work. Several volunteers received 20-year Long Service awards from the National Trust. There is always work to be done at Levant and new volunteers are always welcome during opening hours during the season and on Fridays throughout the year. Besides engine driving and maintenance volunteers give guided tours, including educational school trips, act as stewards, man the office and computer - the list is endless! The National Trust is to be congratulated for its continued support for the Levant Engine project, and for managing the necessary provision of finance and the expertise to enable these works to be carried out. The support of Cornwall County Council and Penwith District Council is also acknowledged.

A website for Levant can be viewed at www.myweb.tiscali.co.uk/levantmine

Contributions by Paul Bonnington, Kenneth Brown, Eric King, Bill Newby, John Potter, Chris Quick, Courtney Rowe and Milton Thomas.

THE MILLENNIUM REFURBISHMENT

NORMAN K. LACKFORD

CHAPTER FOURTEEN

By the end of 1998 the old lady of Levant was showing signs of distress. The condenser and air pump are located in a timber cistern in a pit ten feet deep immediately in front of the iron cylinder. The timber cistern containing the condenser was leaking badly and an examination of the underside revealed the supporting timbers had almost rotted away. Cast concrete pillars and timber supports were put in place to support the cistern for the following year whilst plans were made to replace the cistern at the end of 1999. During the original restoration the cistern had been sealed internally with concrete to overcome the leaks. Another problem that had been apparent for some time was the continual movement of the main cylinder.

The National Trust employed two specialist builders, Colin Rashleigh and Owen Pascoe, to carefully remove the cistern and dig out the concrete surrounding the condenser, whilst John Treloar and myself did the mechanical work. After removal of the cistern, by taking the weight of the condenser on a series of chain blocks, it was possible to look into the void under the main cylinder. It was then that we remembered Milton Thomas's words "Nothing is easy at Levant". We found the cylinder rested on a bedstone over a granite infill supported by a series of granite lintels through which pass the cylinder hold down bolts. All the granite lintels were cracked and starting to collapse, the cylinder retaining bolts were badly rusted and this was the cause of the cylinder movement. As this could affect the structural integrity of the engine house, the National Trust sought advice from a structural engineer who recommended casting a new base for the cylinder, keyed into the engine house walls together with installation of a series of steel girders to support the front of the pit that contained the condenser and air pump.

The stairs and all guards and other obstructions were removed for access and so it began.... The first task was to remove the condenser and air pump assembly. It sounds simple enough but with the sides of the cistern removed we could see that the front wall of the pit was hanging and unstable and had to be propped. The rust joint between the condenser and outlet valve chest manifold took three days to break. We started by drilling and ended by hand chiselling. We found the joint to be a mixture of modern Belzona, used during restoration, covering an original rust joint supported by lead fillets. Having eventually removed the joint, the condenser and air pump were lowered enough to separate from the manifold then be swung aside and lifted to floor level to be parked alongside the flywheel.

The main cylinder complete with valves and manifold had to be raised by about two feet to give

Levant Mine 1992, showing Phillip's Shaft.

This very early view of Levant is taken from an engraving in the Royal Cornwall Museum, by kind permission of the *Royal Institution of Cornwall*.   *Drawn and engraved by W. Willis, Penzance*

Boiler house rebuilding, April 1992.

LEVANT MINE, NEAR St. JUST, CORNWALL.

Engraving by W. Willis, Penzance, c.1847 in the Royal Cornwall Museum, by kind permission of the *Royal Institution of Cornwall*

access to its mounting base. The lift was carried out with a series of chain blocks suspended from the beam. The beam had to be supported at intervals along its entire length to ensure no damage occurred. The bob loft floor, in turn had to be supported from below by props to spread the load (estimated to be about 5 tonnes) as evenly as possible whilst this delicate operation took place. By lifting with a series of chain blocks we could lift and steer the cylinder assembly horizontally and vertically to manoeuvre it away from the unstable pit wall. We raised it to two feet above the bedstone. It is a sad reflection on British industry that the chain blocks, strops and shackles were all made in China. How far have we come since 1840?

With the engine out of the way the real work started. The first job was to remove the bedstone prior to building a new base under the cylinder. With the precarious pit wall shored up, no further lifting capacity within the building and no firm floor or access for a crane, the bedstone had to be broken up in place by drilling prior to its removal. This was very controversial at the time and produced letters to local newspapers but with the lifting and access limitations there was no other option. Volunteers working as individuals may take risks but with current legislation employed staff cannot do so.

After removal of the bedstone a wooden mould was constructed to cast a concrete replacement cylinder mounting. This mounting was keyed into the engine house walls, is two feet deep and the complex matrix of reinforcing rods is a work of art, or as known in Cornwall "a proper job". The new cylinder hold down bolts protrude through this base from the underside. Of course whilst all this took place the cylinder was suspended only two feet above the new base leaving very little space for Colin and Owen to perform their concrete magic. With the base complete the front wall of the pit was supported by girders bolted to stainless steel rods passing through the base to the outside wall of the engine house.

The pit was excavated by a further two or three feet but we found only silt and so two concrete lintels were again cast from wall to wall across the pit to support the new timber cistern. The cistern, made of pine, was prefabricated and pre-drilled in sections, then brought to the engine house as a series of planks to be reassembled in the pit. It copies the original method of construction and dimensions as far as possible but using stainless steel truss rods and galvanised bolts. The stainless nuts had to be specially made, as the original nuts were square. The cistern had to be assembled and bolted together in one day as each joint was sealed with mastic and the complete assembly bolted up before it set. Finally it was coated with several layers of a bitumen compound.

The concrete took 28 days to cure before any load could be placed upon it and during this time the condenser and air pump assembly was de-rusted, cleaned and painted. The original casting was very poor and many holes had been plugged with lead during its construction. The base is a separate casting and both the air pump and the condenser are joined to the base by rust joints.

Once the concrete had cured the air pump/condenser was lowered down into the cistern, and we attempted to align it. We found that it was not possible to align the air pump centrally once the condenser was inserted into the valve chest manifold without the manifold fouling the side of the air pump. This is the reason why the air pump rod has always been offset by a 3" bend immediately under the beam. This has always been a problem causing considerable vibration when the engine is in operation. However during this initial attempt at reassembly we found that the condenser that had, by now, been dry for nearly 6 months, was showing signs of a crack in the rust joint between the condenser and the base. Further examination showed fracture of the original rust joint and so the condenser was separated from its base and pulled back up.

A close examination of the rust joint showed that it appeared to have remained active and had eroded much of the parent metal. The wall thickness of the condenser vessel was less than 1/8" thick in some parts. In view of the poor quality cast iron it was not possible to weld the condenser back to its base so a sleeve was made to bolt them together. The sleeve was machined from a solid steel billet that was so heavy that John Treloar, the National Trust engineer, had to lift it into his lathe with chain blocks. This took a week to turn and bore. The machining of the condenser and its mating face took three days and produced much thick black dust.

As the sleeve had to be turned from solid it was decided to make it eccentric to cure the alignment problem by offsetting the condenser on its base. By reassembling in place in the cistern, all we had to do was align the air pump and rotate the eccentric sleeve for correct condenser alignment. This has enabled us to correctly align the air pump and condenser separately before joining and in consequence we were able to replace the old bent and cracked pump rod with a new straight rod, removing a lot of the vibration that has plagued the engine for many years. Once the sleeve was fitted the joints were completed with a modern epoxy based compound to replicate the original rust joints. The base of the condenser and air pump was bolted through the cistern to a steel channel on the underside with much difficulty (only Colin was slim enough to get under the cistern and turn the bolts). John Treloar made up the clamping ring to bolt around the base of the air pump to enable it to be bolted down in the cistern at low level for increased stability. The underside of the air pump and condenser assembly was sealed to the cistern with an epoxy sealer to prevent any leaks from its fragile cast iron base.

The cylinder and valve chest assembly was finally lowered into place and after the rust joint between the condenser and manifold was completed we were able to reconstruct the floor timbers and remount the valve actuating gear and brake operating arms in their correct positions. The engine finally went back into steam for the first time on a Saturday afternoon in an empty engine house, but we were pleased and very relieved when it ran from the very first pull of the steam valve, with no major problems. All that was left to do was to adjust the valve lift and clearances and cure a small leak on the dump valve that was causing excessive water admission to the condenser.

Finally, after the mess was cleared out and the guards were put back, we ran the engine to hand it back to Levant by setting the steam valve on the peg and leaving it to run by itself. It ran for a full hour on the peg without any adjustment to the steam valve, while John and I sat on the settle, trying not to look concerned. We finally reopened to the public on 10th September and the engine has successfully steamed for the whole of 2001. The only major problem left was the main axle or beam pivot that we suspect to be bent and this was be done during the winter of 2001.

Whilst we were working on the engine, we were still open to the public although much of the access was restricted for safety. During this time the Levant volunteers did a superb job guiding people round the shafts and explaining our problems. I think that it is fair to say that no visitor to Levant left disappointed, even though the engine was not in steam for almost nine months.

Writing this now it seems easy but of course it wasn't, everything was heavy, rusty and coated in grease from a century's work. John Treloar also had to fabricate new mounting brackets for the brake, dump valve and floor mountings, all of which took time and careful measurement. Much of the work was in the condenser pit or under the suspended cylinder assembly with very little access. It took three days crouching in the timber cistern to grind the old rust joints away and three weeks to get clean after. The cast iron dust penetrates overalls, clothes and skin, and leaves a tidemark on the bath that has to be removed with abrasive compound. Quite what the old men who built these engines endured, working with candles, oil lamps and hand tools is beyond belief.

We hope the engine continues to steam for many years as a symbol of respect for their skill and courage. It is a chapter in my life that I shall never regret or forget.

AFTERTHOUGHTS
Having rebuilt the engine and encountered the problems of alignment between the air pump and condenser, I feel that the accident the engine suffered when it burst the flywheel in the 1860s was far worse than we thought. All we know is that the flywheel burst and the engine was repaired by Hocking and Loam. At the time of the accident the engine was winding a single drum and would have been using hemp rope.

I suspect the rope broke, causing the runaway, and the damage was more extensive than realised, and expect that this to be the cause of the broken lintels under the cylinder and the beam axle being bent. The cylinder and piston were probably damaged. All we know for certain is that the cylinder was changed from 24 inches to 27. Whether Harvey's supplied it, cast to suit or a stock replacement is unknown but the cylinder had to fit on the existing bedstone with little tolerance on the mounting holes whilst the air pump and condenser were captive in the floor. Its mounting position appears compromised. I think the beam was moved over to align with the piston rod, thus putting it out of alignment with the air pump resulting in the need to bend the air pump rod to a 3" offset. The other end of the beam is out of alignment with the crankshaft and the sweep rod is not vertical.

After this repair a second winding drum was added and wire ropes were introduced together with a second wheel on the headgear to wind one skip up and one down. A further surprise we found during the rebuild was that the air pump bore was fitted with a brass liner, although it was so discoloured we originally thought it was cast iron. This may also be an 1860 repair as it is unlikely that Harvey's could have turned such a large thin liner in 1840.

The engine worked for 90 years at Levant and in its working life there must have been many changes that have never been recorded. It does seem that, with the exception of the cylinder, piston, valve drive gear and the reversing assembly driven from the crankshaft, all the cast iron parts and much of the wrought iron work is original and owes its origin to Harvey's of Hayle.

Footnote by J. W. F. Treloar, Consultant Engineer, The National Trust

I would like to take this opportunity to express my sincere appreciation for the support of Eric Mason, the Custodian at Levant, the Trevithick Society Volunteers and also Colin Rashleigh and Owen Pascoe, the builders on the above project. I would particularly like to thank Norman Lackford but for whose willingness and enthusiasm this taxing and sometimes hair-raising project would have been even more difficult.

John Treloar

SELECT BIBLIOGRAPHY

Abbott, H. A. Home Office Report on Breaking of a Man Engine at Levant Mine. HMSO 1920.

Barton, Bradford A History of Tin Mining and Smelting in Cornwall. D. Bradford Barton Ltd. 1967.

Barton, D. B. The Cornish Beam Engine. D. Bradford Barton Ltd. 1965.

Beche, Henry T. de la Geological Report on Cornwall, Devon and West Somerset. 1839.

Bosanketh, Edward Tin, A Novel. Justin Brooke. 1983. (New Ed.)

Collins, J. H. Observations on the West of England Mining Region. Transactions of the Royal Geological Society of Cornwall vol. XIV (1912).

Dines, H. G. The Metalliferous Mining Regions of S.W. England. HMSO 1951.

Horsefield, Rev. F. J. Life in a Cornish Village. A.P. Derrington (1984).

Lean, Thomas On the Steam Engines in Cornwall. D. Bradford Barton Ltd. Reprinted 1969.

Noall, Cyril Levant. D. Bradford Barton Ltd. 1970.
Geevor. Geevor Tin Mines Plc. 1983.

Penhale, Jack The Mine under the Sea. J. H. Lake & Co. Ltd. 1962.

Thomas, Herbert Cornish Post & Mining News, 1896.

Young, George, J. The Elements of Mining. McGraw Hill Book Co. Inc. 1932.

Cam Brea Mining Society Newsletters.
The Cornishman newspaper.
Western Morning News newspaper
BBC2 Broadcast 'Yesterday's Witness' on November 1st, 1970. The Levant Mine Disaster'.

STATISTICS

Production at ten year intervals.

Date	Tons of Black Tin	Tons of Copper Ore
1820	—	1,290
1830	—	1,246
1840	32	2,475
1850	359	2,010
1860	244.5	944
1870	127	96
1880	280.5	779
1890	451.5	1,764
1900	548	5,521
1910	347	710
1920	265	—
1929	251.5	—

Number of Employees in various years.

The fact that females and boys are not quoted separately in a number of years does not mean that there were none in the total.

1836	320 men, 44 women, 186 children
1838	550 employees
1841	507 employees
1865	180 men, 17 females, 48 boys
1870	202 employees
1874	300 men
1881	350 employees
1883	298 men, 68 boys and girls
1885	310 men, 31 boys
1894	600 employees
1896	338 men, 66 boys underground
1900	511 men, 165 boys
1905	640 employees
1909	525 employees
1923	150 employees
1930	over 200 employees

The figures, although erratic, do give an idea of the fortunes of the mine and its importance as a source of employment.

Index